The Burnout Solution

Siobhán Murray started in the music industry but was inspired to change her career when she became a single mum to her two sons. She established her psychotherapy and coaching clinic in 2010 and has been delivering bespoke workshops on behavioural change and mindfulness to companies, conferences and events around the country ever since. Siobhan holds a BA in Counselling and Psychotherapy and a Diploma in Mindfulness. She is a Master NLP Practitioner, a certified Life Coach and a Mediator.

The Burnout Solution

12 WEEKS TO A CALMER YOU

Siobhán Murray

Gill Books

Gill Books

Hume Avenue
Park West
Dublin 12
www.gillbooks.ie

Gill Books is an imprint of M.H. Gill and Co.

978 07171 8094 3

Design and print origination by O'K Graphic Design,Dublin
Edited by Jane Rogers
Proofread by Ellen Christie
Printed by TJ International, Cornwall

This book is typeset in 11/17 pt Bembo with headings in Freight Light.

A CIP catalogue record for this book is available from the British Library.

5 4 3

Acknowledgements

When I embarked on writing this book, I never thought I would learn as much as I did about burnout and how it can affect each and every one of us. I thought I had pretty much all angles covered but I can honestly say that in the process of writing this book I delved back into the furnace once more, and learnt so much more about why living a life with self-care ingrained in our daily existence is so important. We never stop learning and for that I am eternally grateful.

At the beginning of 2017, I put on my Vision Board (among other goals) that I wanted to write a book. I wasn't sure at that time how I was going to go about transforming my vision into a reality but I believed every day that it would happen. Towards the end of 2017 I received a call from Sarah Liddy, who would become my Commissioning Editor (a very patient commissioning editor at that), and that phone call marked the beginning of my vision becoming a reality. So, from the bottom of my heart (and Vision Board), thank you Sarah Liddy for making that call, for facilitating my vision until it became a reality, for being so patient with me, for guiding me and for just being a fantastic lady! Thank you to Sheila Armstrong my editor, Teresa Daly for my beautiful book cover and Ellen Monnelly for organising all my publicity – a tribe of ladies that supported my vision!

The biggest thank you has to go my two boys, Seán and Charlie, who have taught me so much since the day they were born and continue to do so every day. Children are sent to teach us; we are merely here to guide and nurture them. I am a kinder, more compassionate human being because of these two people, and I will forever be grateful I got to be their mother, even when they drive me to distraction!

Jean Murray, my mother and friend, thank you for being you! For cooking meatballs and baking cakes so I could feed the boys and write and work! You are quietly strong, a gentle lady and everything I'm not. Not a week goes by without my Auntie Trisha calling me – to hear her say 'I'm so proud of you' makes my heart melt, so thank you Trisha for believing in my dreams and visions. I'm blessed to have you in my corner.

To all the clients I have had the privilege of working with, past, present and future, it is an honour to share your lives and have your trust. I couldn't think of a job I would rather have – thank you so much. I hope that in sharing some of your stories readers will identify with you and know they too can make the changes they want, to build their resilience and know they are not alone.

I am so blessed to have the most amazing Girl Tribe from around the world, who keep me grounded, love me, accept me and champion me as I do them. Friendships, new or old, are the cornerstone to healthy living – thank you Pam, Emma, Victoria, Laura, Orla, Alison, Lynn, Fiona M, Ali, Claire O'G, Mette, Christine T, Joy, Pei Ching, Dayse, Truly Julie and Jane. And not forgetting the amazing Boy Tribe I have, the incredible men who collect my boys for matches and training when I can't. It took me a long time to learn how to ask for help – don't take as long as I did!

Thank you to my super organised V.A., Juliette, for our weekly chats and for keeping one step ahead of me, I'd be lost without you!

Lastly, this isn't so much a thank you as a shout out. At times, when I struggled juggling writing, working, mothering and various other projects, I focused on a beautiful young girl who inspires me, Freya O'Doherty, and my stunning friend, Alison Kelly, who are both fighting strong against cancer. Nobody should have to fight this disease, not at thirteen years old nor at forty-two while a mother of two. Neither of you will ever understand how much you helped me in writing this book – you are both incredible.

And finally, thank you lovely reader, my hope for you in reading this book is that you recognise the signs of burnout, reverse them and build a big fat bank of resilience so that when the curveballs of life get too much you are well equipped to deal with them. Thank you!

Contents

Introduction

From music industry to coaching psychotherapist

F irst let me start by saying that this book is not just about me and my life, and I don't claim to have *all* the answers. It was, however, my personal experiences of pushing myself beyond my limitations (which eventually led to my burnout), of how it affected not just me but those around me, and of learning the hard way how to manage it that made me want to write about burnout. I wanted to share with you what I've learned about it, what the signs are, and simple, practical and inexpensive ways to manage it, in the hope that it will help you recognise, recover and build resilience around burnout.

I was raised an only child of separated parents. For me this was a lonely place. I read a lot (and still do) and spent a huge amount of time around adults – but as much as I was loved, I was aware that my voice wasn't as important as theirs. When I was six years old my mother had a brain haemorrhage and the impact of this was devastating on everyone.

She was temporarily paralysed on one side of her body and had to stay in hospital for what seemed to a young girl of six a very long time. Looking back, I now realise it was during this time that I learned to 'not use my voice'. The focus of life was on my mother and everyone else had to be quiet around her. I learned to get on with things even if I didn't know what I was doing. I became solution-focused rather than problem-focused. There was little time to be focused on me. I don't say that with any self-pity; it is just plain fact. But the seeds had already been sown of not wanting to draw attention to myself, of wanting to be 'really good', of viewing outside signs of recognition as a form of internal self-worth.

I was struggling at school. Studying was a strange activity that all my peers did but I had no idea how to do. I had been told in primary school that I wouldn't amount to anything and I wasn't very good at school. These became my underlying limiting self-beliefs. The more I didn't ask for help, the more trouble I seemed to be getting myself into in school. But the habit of not wanting to demand attention as a child because I felt that my mother needed it more was going to end up causing me even more trouble. Sometime around early Sixth Year I ended up feeling worthless, despondent and downright miserable. Without my mother's permission or approval, I decided to leave school.

This has been the biggest contributor to my burnout. Not completing my Leaving Cert made me feel that I had to prove myself twice as much as everyone else; it made me feel not good enough for whatever job I did; and it contributed to never feeling good enough in who I was. I always had this underlying feeling that I would be 'found out', a form of Imposter Syndrome. So I always felt utterly stressed in working environments, regardless of whether the tasks themselves were stressful.

In my early twenties I worked for one of the biggest music promoters in Ireland. I knew nothing about the industry other than the bands, I was a terrible PA, and I would say yes instead of no in order to put others' requests first, and this meant that I was in a constant state of 'catch-up'.

A few years later I moved to London to seek pastures new within the same industry (I also thought being somewhere else would mean I'd feel different). In order to prove myself, I worked incredibly hard; I took on projects that were out of my comfort zone, believing that this would show my employers I was indispensable (mistake #1). I bought my first home at the age of 24 when most of my peers were still thinking about where to go on a Friday night. I was slowly conditioning myself to thinking that being 'busy' and 'achieving' was a sign of success.

I describe life as a large pot on the stove. We start with the pot, which is filled with water (a sense of calmness), and we learn to add to the pot increasing responsibilities, financial commitments, children, jobs, relationships, family, but what we don't do is learn to take things out of the pot to make room for the new things to fit in. This means the water starts to overflow and spill out of the pot. In simple terms, that means the sense of calm leaves us. If we keep putting things into the pot and don't take the time to remove some stuff, there is a big possibility that we end up overwhelmed, burnt-out, dissatisfied, disillusioned, cranky, unmotivated, sleeping poorly, with diminished concentration and a general feeling of lethargy.

By the time I was 28 years old I was a bit lost. Work was good and I owned my own home, but I wasn't happy. I moved home to Dublin (again thinking another move would change how I felt) and over the course of the next few years I worked for a number of companies. All the time I didn't think to take anything out of my 'pot'. In 2005 I added my first non-negotiable responsibility to my pot – the birth of my first son. Now I had a demanding job, a mortgage, gym membership, a car (still somewhat above my means), nights out and my son. And still I didn't take anything out of the 'pot'.

I could feel myself slipping, but rather than address it, I would have another glass of wine. If I had admitted that I couldn't juggle it all, that I was on the cusp of burnout, then in my eyes I would be admitting failure (mistake #2 – not asking for help). My work began to slip and I know I was very tetchy. I would sleep whenever I could, not the lovely 'nap' sleep but the 'I'm getting into bed with the duvet over my head' sleep. The unmotivated sleep.

In 2007 my second non-negotiable responsibility arrived – my second son, Charlie. And again I didn't take anything from the now overflowing pot. I returned to work after a very short maternity leave. This was now me at burnout. A single parent with a baby and a toddler, a demanding career, etc., etc. Looking back, even if I didn't have the boys, I know I would still have burnt-out. In reality I was so used to working in order to prove myself that I was never really happy. I was always in a state of stress, I drank too much to try to make myself believe I was doing okay. If I didn't change something about the way I worked then, children or no children, I was going to hit burnout.

I left corporate employment and bought a franchise, thinking that this would be the answer to my problems. A combination of being burnt-out, not addressing how I felt and still working the way I always had, meant that I simply didn't have the energy I needed to put into the job to make it the success I wanted. So now, to add to my existing burnout, I had a failed business and I didn't have a huge amount of money coming in.

But it did mean that I started to think about what I am good at and what I really like to do. I thought about going back to school to do my Leaving Cert, but in the end I started to look at going to college. My biggest limiting self-belief – not being good enough – was going to be confronted head-on. I started an introductory course in Psychotherapy, and with the help of the lecturer I started a Diploma in Psychotherapy and Counselling. Then I continued my studies, obtaining a degree in Integrative Counselling and Psychotherapy. The girl who didn't feel good enough, who hadn't completed her Leaving Cert, now had a degree.

It was around this time I did the first best thing I could do for myself (and those around me). I stopped drinking alcohol. Not a lot of people knew it, but in order to mask the feeling of being overwhelmed, for years I drank, and I drank a lot. I also drank to mask the fact I was not the extrovert that everyone thought I was – I am an introvert, a very happy introvert! By the time I quit, I was drinking two bottles of wine every night, not including the nights I went out, when I would drink far more. And yes, I did that while holding down a good job and raising two boys.

I say this not because I am proud of it or don't care what other people think, but because it happened and it's part of my story. I am writing about it in the hope that some of you may identify with some of my behaviours and know that you are not alone. I write about it because I care. For me, drinking was the first big thing I took out of my overflowing 'pot'. It didn't happen straightaway, but gradually I started to feel slightly calmer. Because I wasn't drinking, I stopped going out as much as I had done, I was present with the boys and life wasn't as overwhelming as before. Because I wasn't drinking I was sleeping better and even eating better. I even went on to stop smoking and take up running. All of these were intentional behavioural changes I took responsibility for.

Something else I did for myself was not actually intentional. One of the criteria for doing the diploma in Psychotherapy was that you had to undergo a minimum of 50 hours of personal therapy over the duration of the course. So, unbeknownst to me, while learning about something I loved, I was also working on identifying and changing some of my behaviours that weren't serving me well, and I started to learn, understand and practise self-care and self-love. Through the course of this book you're going to hear me say those words quite a lot, so get used to reading them – self-care and self-love!

Since qualifying with a BA in Counselling and Psychotherapy and setting up my own private practice, I've trained as a master practitioner in NLP (neuro-linguistic programming); I am a certified mediator and work with separating couples; I'm a mindfulness practitioner; I regularly speak at corporate events about burnout; I am a certified personal trainer and am starting my masters in Positive Psychology and Psychology of Coaching.

In giving you a glimpse of how my life became hectic and overwhelming, I hope to show you that burnout is not just something that happens to people in the highly professional sector – it can affect anyone at any stage of their life. Burnout can be bubbling away under the surface and be triggered by something completely unrelated, for example work, family, friends or a combination of some or all of them.

My aim is that as you read through this book, you will have a greater understanding of the signs of burnout, be able to identify its symptoms and causes, and use the practical tools and exercises I recommend to aid your healthy recovery and put systems in place to ensure you don't end up burnt-out.

How to use this book

've written this book to help you get an understanding of what exactly burnout is, what the signs and symptoms are, and how to reduce and recover from the impact it may be having on your life. I work with clients suffering from burnout, who see me one-to-one in my coaching practice, through a 12-week programme to help them understand how they have ended up burnt-out and what behaviours they can change to prevent it from happening again.

This book will help you identify the warning signals of burnout and put in place strategies that will work for you to prevent burnout. However, this is not a quick-fix sticking plaster to get you through a bad phase; it's a combination of personal experiences, tried and tested practices, logic and straightforward honesty rolled into a book to help you manage you.

This is your personal 12-week programme designed for you to work through and refer back to whenever you start to feel overwhelmed with life. The book looks at ways burnout affects you both personally and professionally. Not all burnout is the result of a high-pressured job; it can be caused by situations in your personal life too.

The plan is laid out in twelve chapters, one chapter for each week. Each week you will learn new tools and techniques that act like 'layers' you can use to begin rebuilding a calmer, happier and more controlled life. Once you've worked through the first few weeks and start to understand what may have contributed to your burnout, you then start to add on the new 'layers' to support you in implementing positive changes.

Although this is structured as a 12-week programme, it is by no means set in stone that you must complete each stage in a week. Some weeks you may find there is a lot to digest and some weeks you might sail through it. Take your time. This is your book. You don't have a deadline to meet and you're not in a competition with anyone else! If you feel you'd like to take longer working through some chapters, then take longer. This is not a quick-fix solution; your burnout didn't happen overnight, and neither will recovery – it takes time too. You are going to be challenging your old learned behaviours and embedding new positive behaviours into your life. Change is not always comfortable, so be kind and gentle to yourself and remember, no matter what – you're doing a great job!

For example, you may read through the section on sleep and realise that you are doing well in that area at the moment. If that is the case, then simply move on to the next chapter. With each week of the programme you will be learning to understand yourself more, and the better you understand yourself, the better able you will be to implement the changes you need to reduce and eliminate the symptoms of burnout.

Remember, this is not a race – no one is checking to see how long it takes you to complete each week. The weeks are merely guidelines to help you work through your changes with the least amount of perceived stress. Enjoy the process and know that you are implementing these changes for you.

Burnout is not a place of no return. In fact, if managed correctly, it can be a catalyst for positive change in your life. If, while reading this book, you identify with some of the symptoms of burnout, take the time to do a life audit and use this opportunity to make changes.

I would ask that once you begin reading this book, if you don't use one already, start a journal. Write down how you feel and use the guided questions to track your progress over time. There are lots of examples and worksheets to fill out in each chapter. You can either write in this book or use them as templates and write directly into your journal. There is also a mood questionnaire you can fill in, which is a good way of keeping track of how you are coping. What way you choose to write down and track the thoughts in your head is entirely up to you, but I strongly recommend you write them down. It's a great way of tracking how you feel and seeing the changes you are making for yourself.

There are so many positive reasons to keep a journal or, in plain English, to write things down. The main reason I do it is to get thoughts and worries out of my head, where they run around bumping into each other, and each time they do, the worry or thought seems to grow and has a tendency to become slightly overwhelming. Writing things down gets these thoughts and worries out of my head and onto paper, and in turn frees up my head space so that I can manage them rather than them managing me. I've dedicated a whole section to journalling and its benefits (see Week 11).

Journalling allows the brain to generate clarity and congruence (I love that word!). Writing down what is going on in our head allows us to identify what is real and what is not. And in turn it will give you the ability to see what needs to be changed in your life and figure out what is working or not working for you. The list of benefits are endless. We can hold on to incredibly negative thoughts in our minds that can stay put for days or even years. When we learn to write honestly and with personal responsibility, it frees up so much head space for us to move on, let go and create the environment we want.

As a last note on this, I would recommend journalling with pen and paper rather than technology. Human beings struggle to retain information;

we have a tendency to forget a lot of what we hear and read unless it strikes an emotional cord with us. Writing things down increases brain development and memory, something that typing into our phones or computers does not do.

Finally, all the resources and exercises in this book are also available online at www.twistingthejar.com.

MOOD QUESTIONAIRE

Please read each statement and circle a number 0, 1, 2 or 3 which indicates how much the statement applied to you **over the past week**. There are no right or wrong answers. Do not spend too much time on any statement.

The rating scale is as follows:

0   Did not apply to me at all

1   Applied to me to some degree, or some of the time

2   Applied to me to a considerable degree or a good part of time

3   Applied to me very much or most of the time

1   I found it hard to wind down.

0   1   2   3

2   I was aware of dryness of my mouth.

0   1   2   3

3   I couldn't seem to experience any positive feeling at all.

0   1   2   3

4   I experienced breathing difficulty (e.g. excessively rapid breathing, breathlessness in the absence of physical exertion).

0   1   2   3

5   I found it difficult to work up the initiative to do things.

0   1   2   3

6   I tended to over-react to situations.

0   1   2   3

7 I experienced trembling (e.g. in the hands).

| 0 | 1 | 2 | 3 |

8 I felt that I was using a lot of nervous energy.

| 0 | 1 | 2 | 3 |

9 I was worried about situations in which I might panic and make a fool of myself.

| 0 | 1 | 2 | 3 |

10 I felt that I had nothing to look forward to.

| 0 | 1 | 2 | 3 |

11 I found myself getting agitated.

| 0 | 1 | 2 | 3 |

12 I found it difficult to relax.

| 0 | 1 | 2 | 3 |

13 I felt down-hearted and blue.

| 0 | 1 | 2 | 3 |

14 I was intolerant of anything that kept me from getting on with what I was doing.

| 0 | 1 | 2 | 3 |

15 I felt I was close to panic.

| 0 | 1 | 2 | 3 |

16 I was unable to become enthusiastic about anything.

| 0 | 1 | 2 | 3 |

17 I felt I wasn't worth much as a person.

    0   1   2   3

18 I felt that I was rather touchy.

    0   1   2   3

19 I was aware of the action of my heart in the absence of physical exertion (e.g. sense of heart rate increase, heart missing a beat).

    0   1   2   3

20 I felt scared without any good reason.

    0   1   2   3

21 I felt that life was meaningless.

    0   1   2   3

Week 1

Are you burnt-out?

'A state of physical, emotional, and mental exhaustion caused by long term
involvement in emotionally demanding situations.'

AYALA PINES AND ELLIOT ARONSON

BURNOUT: MYTH OR FACT?

Burnout is real, very real, and it is a product of living in a state of
continual stress. It is the feeling you have when you've been pushing
yourself too hard for too long, when the fast pace of the twenty-first
century is never-ending, and you just can't keep up any more. In today's
world, working long hours, being a full-time working parent or juggling
being a family caregiver with numerous other life demands is no longer for
the small minority, it's an expectation of our society. And this comes at a
price: our emotional, physical and spiritual health.

Burnout is a relatively new term, but we are hearing it more and more
frequently. It was coined in the 1970s by American psychologist Herbert
Freudenberger, and it was initially used to describe what was happening
to people who worked in what are considered 'high-stress' careers, such as
doctors, nurses, lawyers and high-level professionals who put their career
and success before their own self-care. A lot has changed since the 1970s

and burnout is no longer a term exclusively used for the elite professions. It can and does affect anyone – primary school teachers, stay-at-home mothers, third-level students, married couples, single people, people with children, people wanting children, grandparents ... The list goes on and on.

I would like to note at this point that just because someone works more than 60 hours a week, runs a family home, completes ultra-marathons and has a smile on their face, doesn't automatically mean that they're going to suffer from burnout. Some people thrive on being busy and have built-in coping mechanisms to allow them to function at a higher pace. Others simply do not.

> Burnout can be described as being driven by an ideal, working harder and harder, putting one's own needs last, feeling miserable, isolated and denying what is happening, the death of one's values leading to cynicism, frustration and disengagement, feelings of inner emptiness and finally both physical and mental collapse.

It has always amazed me how we can inherit behavioural traits that are glued into our DNA. I was raised an only child, but at the age of 30, I found out that I have a sister, a full older sister, a DNA copy of me. Before I met her I had so many questions in my head – would we look alike? Would we like each other? Would we have anything in common? My sister was born in the London, raised in Wales and later in New Zealand. She was brought up Church of England and I was raised Catholic. There are so many factors that separate us, yet our DNA makes us so similar in so many ways. We are both left handed, have similar gestures and sense of humour, we can finish each other's sentences and we problem solve in a similar way.

Carl Jung, the Swiss psychologist who founded the school of analytical psychology and who has been a constant source of inspiration for psychologists and psychotherapists, proposed a theory of the **collective**

unconscious. This refers to structures of the unconscious mind that are shared among beings of the same species, i.e. humans. In simple terms, he believed that all human beings have the same thoughts stored in our unconscious minds which are there from birth. These thoughts are rooted in the deepest part of the unconscious mind and have not been put there by personal experience. Collective unconscious is defined as 'a part of the unconscious mind, incorporating patterns of memories, instincts, and experiences common to all mankind' (*Collins English Dictionary*).

If this is so, why do we not all act the same? What makes one person more able to manage life's stresses than another? How come some people are born with the ability to practise personal compassion and others are not? Why do we sometimes sail through life, even when we have lots to manage, and at other times just get completely overwhelmed by the enormity of life? Thankfully, we don't all consciously think the same; we all have our unique individual qualities that make us who we are, and therefore we respond differently to similar events and stresses. This book doesn't seek to challenge Carl Jung and his incredible contribution to the understanding of the mind; his teachings and theories have been part of the core of my self-care and emotional wellbeing. But because we all respond in different ways to different situations, regardless of our collective unconscious, I want to share with you not just the signs and symptoms of the ever-growing epidemic of burnout in modern society, but also some simple tools that you can begin using straight away.

Along with practising self-care and self-love, if you are in any doubt as to whether you are suffering from burnout, either personally or professionally, please seek medical advice. This book is a handbook to help and is not in any way intended to replace the expertise of the medical profession.

This is your first week and before we even start looking at what you can do to recover from burnout, it's important to understand exactly what the term burnout means, where it comes from and how to find out if are you already burnt-out or heading towards burnout. Let's look at the signs and symptoms of burnout and what specifically causes it.

According to the *International Classification of Diseases*, the following are symptoms of burnout:

- muscle aches and pains
- dizziness
- tension headaches
- sleep disturbance
- physical and mental exhaustion and fatigue after minimal effort
- an inability to relax
- irritability
- inability to recover after rest, relaxation or entertainment.

The ICD-10 states that these symptoms need to last for at least three months and should not be confused with depression.

AM I BURNT-OUT OR DEPRESSED?

While this book is not focused on depression, I feel it is important to talk about it and how it differs from burnout. It is often assumed that burnout and depression are two different words with the same meaning. However, although the two have several symptoms in common, they are very much two separate conditions that have differing diagnoses.

Being burnt-out is a physical, mental and emotional state that is caused by severe stress either at home or at work. Depression, on the other hand, is defined as a 'clinical behavioural disorder' affecting a person's mood. If you are experiencing burnout, you may be more at risk of experiencing (short-term) or developing depression rather than the other way around; one of the symptoms of burnout is a change in your mood, whereas it is rare that you will become burnt-out as a result of experiencing depression.

If you are suffering from depression, you may not be able to see the good in anything that is happening in your life. A wonderful animated video created by Matthew Johnson, *I Had a Black Dog*, cleverly explains what living with depression is like and I strongly recommend you have a look at it.

> If you feel in any way that you are suffering from depression, please, please, please seek help. Visit your GP, speak to a family member or friend, or see a therapist. Do not feel that you can cope alone.

So what is depression? It is a complex condition which involves both your internal coping skills and external influences. It is diagnosed by a medical professional when a person has a depressed mood (feelings of being sad, empty, tearful or lonely), or has lost interest and enjoyment in their activities. Other symptoms of depression are:

- changes in appetite
- sleep problems (either insomnia or excessive sleep)
- fatigue
- agitation
- feelings of worthlessness
- difficulty concentrating
- recurrent thoughts of suicide or death.

If you can identify with any of these it does not necessarily mean there is a problem. As with burnout, difficult situations in life can make us feel out of character. The important question with depression is one of intensity and duration. You may be suffering from depression when your symptoms last for more than two weeks and when they are severe enough to cause either significant personal suffering or the loss of the ability to function normally.

HOW IS DEPRESSION DIFFERENT?

Burnout is caused by living life in a state of continual stress. Depression, however, is different because it is not necessarily the result of prolonged periods of stress and anxiety. Of course it *can* result from excess stress, but depression can also be the result of a *lack* of stimulation, such as a lack of social connections. Depression may also be caused by numerous other factors: genetically inherited; medical issues; taking certain medications (there are so many medications on the market now that have side effects of depression); or even a traumatic event like a relationship break–up, losing your job, moving countries or a death in the family.

The important part of understanding the difference between burnout and depression is that while making physical and emotional changes to how you respond to the underlying issues causing your burnout can often be enough to recover from it, recovering from depression is much more complex process. Your recovery from burnout can be managed by reducing stress in your life and by making adjustments to your lifestyle, all of which are covered in this book. Although it may take a while to notice the changes, burnout ends as soon as positive changes to your lifestyle are implemented. With mild to severe depression, while lifestyle changes are vital, you may also require medical interventions.

◇ Depression is a clinical disorder, unlike burnout, which is a result of extreme stress.

◇ Burnout is usually more often work-related than is depression.

◇ Depression is a more serious condition that has longer-lasting and more frequently recurring symptoms than burnout.

◇ Depression is best managed with either medical intervention and/or psychotherapy, while burnout is managed by stress reduction and changes in lifestyle.

THE SIGNS AND SYMPTOMS OF BURNOUT

Dr Glenn Roberts uses a system of measuring possible burnout by the obvious changes that may be happening to us. He breaks them down into four areas:

- changes in our behaviour
- changes in our feelings
- changes in our thinking
- changes in our health.

Changes in our behaviour, feelings, thinking and health can obviously occur in short bursts when we have taken on too much and stretched ourselves too thinly. We can become irritable and tired if we are working on a month-end report or studying for exams, but we generally return to normal when the event/project is over. However, look back over the last few months or even years and ask yourself:

Changes in behaviour:

- Have you been working from home more often, even after doing a full day in the office?
- Found it harder to keep on top of things even though you are spending time on them?
- Struggling with making simple decisions or problem solving?
- Not satisfied with the work you're doing?
- Spending more time working than socialising/seeing friends?
- Find doing regular activities a chore?
- Increased your caffeine and/or alcohol intake?
- Become more dependent on fast food?

Changes in feelings:

●   Noticed that you've lost your sense of humour?

●   Feel angry a lot of the time?

●   Feel like a failure?

●   Feel responsible for everything?

Changes in thinking:

●   Find it hard to work through tasks?

●   Struggle concentrating?

●   Play out scenarios negatively in your head?

●   Think everyone and everything is conspiring against you?

Changes in health:

●   Recurring colds and flus?

●   Poor sleep?

●   Cry more easily?

●   Feel tired even after sleeping?

The symptoms of burnout don't happen overnight; they develop slowly, so you might not even be aware of them to start with. It's like a domino effect – one goes down and the rest follow. The good news is that all these symptoms can be dealt with and you can put new systems in place with which to change how you respond to life. If you can identify with some of these symptoms, the chances are you've been living in a reactive state of mind. It's now time to switch that to learning to respond efficiently.

The foundations of my burnout were established in early childhood and then gradually crept up on me during my twenties and thirties. My burnout was triggered by the pressure of having a family and still trying to meet my self-imposed demands at work. Looking back, I can see now how the external pressures of my limiting self-belief – not knowing how to cope with a demanding job, a big mortgage, childcare costs, being a single parent, trying to maintain a pre-children social life *and* be the best parent I could to two small boys – was beginning to get too much. I was trying to be all things to all people without actually listening to what I needed to be for myself. Because I lived my life with damaging limiting self-beliefs (I talk about these later) I was becoming more and more resentful about everything I had to do. I felt totally undervalued at work and at home. Now I see people, especially women, striving to juggle a career with family life, meet the expectations of friends and family and co-workers, and how the pressure to meet these external demands causes inevitable burnout.

I probably work longer hours now than I did in my corporate days, but now I am in charge of what I do and when I do it. There are times when I juggle raising my darling boys – I watch them play as many matches as I can – while working with clients, working on various projects, speaking at conferences and events, lecturing, seeing friends (sometimes connecting with friends via technology is enough), writing articles (and books!), training and running; and I have a habit of finding something new to study every winter. My days are full and busy and sometimes I, too, can overstretch myself!

Now for some full disclosure! When I embarked on writing this book, I felt somewhat disingenuous and out of place. I can stand in front of hundreds of people speaking about burnout and how to manage and reverse its effects, and I work every day coaching clients dealing with stress, but I felt slightly disconnected talking about my own experience. You see, my experience with burnout was so many years ago and I have, over time, cultivated a personal self-care plan that keeps me on an evenish keel. I didn't want to write this and say, 'Do as I do, and you'll be great' or 'Your recovery from burnout will be easy.' Well, as luck would have it, the universe decided that in order for me to write this book and be as congruent as I can, it would throw me into a temporary state of continuous stress and I started to experience once again the signs of burnout that affected me.

During the time I wrote this book the following events took place:

- I watched a close friend have her whole life rearranged in a matter of seconds when her 12-year-old daughter was diagnosed with stage four brain cancer.

- I committed to working on a television documentary looking at stress and its effects.

- My father was taken into hospital for three weeks in December, which made Santa's job quite hard as all my spare time was taken up with going to the hospital.

- I spoke at numerous corporate and wellness events.

- I maintained a six-day week of coaching clients (I work from home so that I'm here for the boys).

- I completed my Personal Training Certificate.

- I moved to a new house (unexpectedly) in the snow. (Never. Ever. Again.)

- I lectured at a college two or three times a week.

- I had family to visit in the middle of utter chaos.

- I did my absolute best to be present for the boys when I felt pulled in every direction.

- I tried to keep my self-care plan and sense of humour intact.

Along with all this I ran my home, did my best to be the friend to others they were to me and kept a smile on my face. I was like a swan, gliding on the water but paddling like f★★k underneath.

So what happened? Initially, not a lot. I got a bit cranky with immediate family. To start with I was trying to get Christmas going, and for me

Christmas is a big deal. I was travelling to St James's Hospital to visit my
father and speak to his medical team, and in some ways I was resentful
that I was not getting to find the boys' Christmas presents, the stocking
fillers and the endless boxes of Roses I didn't need. I ended up putting up
the Christmas tree at 2 a.m. as that was the only time I could find to get
it decorated. Some days I wrote until midnight and got up at 5.15 a.m.
I drank too much coffee, skipped breakfast and ate bowls of dried bran
flakes by the bucket load. I missed running and training sessions and instead
researched and wrote this book. The more I researched the importance of
sleep, the more sleep I missed! I felt bloated and my eating habits suffered.
I had headaches and if my nearest and dearest heard me say, 'I'll be with
you in a minute, I'm just working' once, they heard me say it a hundred
times. I stayed present with all my clients and held and cherished them as
much as I always do. I stayed up late researching because my old habit of
perfectionism reared her head and every time I felt I'd finished a chapter,
I'd find something else I wanted to put in. My limiting self-beliefs rallied
round to try to convince me that I couldn't write a book and these beliefs
paired up for a double date with procrastination. My self-care got tossed
aside as if I didn't matter and in the short time it took to reach the early
stages of burnout, my body had noticed the effects hugely. I'm glad to say
that the old self-care tool box is being slowly restored back to normal – in
fact, I'll probably add a few more tools to ensure I've an even wider choice
in future. Do I regret saying yes to writing this book and catapulting myself
back into a high-stress situation which unleashed a lot of my limiting self-
beliefs? Absolutely not! It has given me a refresher insight into how easily
burnout can sneak up on you, and the emotional and physical impact it has
had on my body. It has, in some strange way that only the universe knows,
made it easier to write this book for you.

Now while all that may sound exhausting and as if I need a serious life
audit myself, the difference for me *now* is that I have my self-care plan

already in place. I know what works for me and it will be easier to go back to being kind to myself. I can work to my schedule: if I want to work four evenings a week until 9 p.m., I can; if I want to take time off to be there for the boys, I can. I get to work on projects knowing there's a light at the end of the tunnel. I know when to turn my phone to 'do not disturb', which I do regularly. If I have a late night working (or a few weeks in this case), I ensure that the next few nights' sleep is back on track. The tools, tips and techniques I describe in the book are here because they work. They have been researched, practised and developed in order to work. You may think at times that they are screamingly obvious and extremely simple – in fact too simple to actually work. You're wrong. We human beings have a fabulous ability to complicate our own lives unnecessarily and are surprised when we find out that simple changes to how we live can have huge positive consequences.

We all have our days (or weeks) when our lives get thrown into chaos and we feel a bit at sea, and that's normal as long as you can slot back into your routine and sense of order within a short timeframe. However, if you feel out of sorts and not firing on all cylinders, take a few minutes to compare youself today to where you were six months or a year ago and see what changes there might be. Some of the signs of burnout are not so obvious. Here are just a few:

- **You don't have a routine.** If you find that you're missing, say, gym classes in favour of work, not eating well, not sleeping or resting enough, avoiding your social network of friends or keeping a schedule that's all over the place and constantly playing catch-up, you may be experiencing one of the first signs of burnout – whatever self-care you had has goes out of the window.

- **You find you are becoming uncharacteristically negative.** If you routinely feel like nothing you do matters or can change the situation you're in, you may be developing a burnt-out attitude.

- **You've got the attention span of a toddler.** Okay, so this is one that can happen to the best of us on any given day, so I'm not talking about your one-off days but when you start to feel like this every day. If you're struggling to focus on one thing at a time or complete a task without your mind wandering and you end up checking your social media apps or you start picking up other projects midstream, you're in risk of putting your body's natural stress response under pressure, which can halt your brain's concentration process. When you're under stress, your senses become hypersensitive to what's happening around you (I've a whole chapter on stress and what it does to our body), and while this hypersensitivity is extremely helpful when you're in real danger, continued levels of it messes up your concentration.

- **You're numbing the pain.** If you find you're drinking more alcohol than you used to, eating more junk food, smoking or taking recreational drugs, you could be trying to satisfy your body's natural needs with cheap, unhealthy, readily available crap. For example, if you're living on multiple cups of coffee each day instead of eating well for energy, your body can only sustain that for so long. Trust me, I know.

- **You've forgotten how to switch off.** If the only time you're not busy is when you're sleeping (which, although I'm passionate about it, is not the only way to rest), you may be depriving yourself of much-needed awake rest time and thus preventing your brain from relaxing the stress response. When was the last time you just sat and relaxed without using mental energy worrying about something or didn't have your computer or mobile phone open all evening? If the answer is 'I can't remember', it's a sign that you don't know how to switch off.

You are amazing. You have got this far in your life, with all its ups and downs; you've adapted to changes, whether you realise it or not, and have taken on extra work either at home or work (which may have contributed to burnout). You are, to all intents and purposes, a superhero — we all are. But when you try to juggle more demands than you can emotionally or physically handle for extended periods of time, you eventually burn out.

It's also important to take into consideration that how we are brought up impacts how we view our ability to manage ourselves in adult life. Someone who appears to have it all — a successful career, a family and a great social life — may indeed have it all, but appearances can cover a multitude of issues that can cause burnout. I have seen many clients with a successful career who are perceived as having a good handle on their lives, but are actually struggling with managing life. Their childhood learned behaviours, which may have been created out of a need for emotional survival, do not always work in the adult world. Instead, they are constantly in a state of high alert. I like to describe this as living like a light bulb. Think of a light bulb being switched on and being left on — it eventually overheats and may even explode. The light bulb is designed to be switched on for short periods of time; this is when it works at its optimum level. For it to function properly it needs to be switched off to cool down before it's switched back on again. If it is left on indefinitely it will overheat and finally blow up. Your body is just like the light bulb. It needs to be able to switch off after being on high alert (i.e. after a stressful situation) and cool down so it can recharge. When your body is recharging, your blood pressure lowers, your heart rate returns to normal, your breathing evens out and your body relaxes. Your body sleeps better, which is another key component in recharging, both physically and mentally.

When you are experiencing a stressor and you are in a state of high alert, your body is producing cortisol, adrenaline and other hormones to react to the situation. The problem we are facing in the twenty-first century is that we are nearly always switched on in a reactive rather than responsive way. With the constant ability to be contacted 24/7 through technology and the increasing need to be seen as always working, our bodies are finding it harder to recognise the difference between an emergency (fight-or-flight mode) and general stress, which will pass. Our bodies are living in a heightened state of stress for long periods of time, which we are not physically or mentally capable of doing.

As you can see, there is an enormous impact on your body both inside and out from existing in a constant or near-constant state of stress, which can lead to burnout. Being nearly always switched on has become an addiction, one which we are not even aware we have.

Week 2

How did you become burnt-out?

Last week we looked at what causes burnout. This week we start to explore how *you* may have ended up burnt-out. Is it your work or personal life that is the root cause of how you are feeling? The burnout quiz on the next page will help you to gauge if you may be heading for, or already experiencing, burnout. We look at what you can do if your burnout is being caused by your current work situation and when simply changing your job isn't an option right now for you. We look at the obvious factors in your life and the not-so-obvious ones that may have caused you to burn out.

CAUSES OF BURNOUT

The causes of burnout can be divided into some obvious factors (work, family commitments) and some not-so-obvious ones (when your personal values and core beliefs do not align with what you do in your job, in your friendships or even your family).

I like to think of burnout not as the result of not being able to cope with life but as the result of not having the personal tools, techniques and boundaries to manage the demands of life.

There are many contributing factors to burnout. The most obvious one is your job, and while that can have the biggest part to play in burnout there are also other factors to take into consideration. Sleep, nutrition, relationships, clutter in your life, your childhood, limiting self-beliefs, past experiences, lifestyle, perfectionism and fear of change are just some of the other factors that can contribute to reaching burnout. Knowing the signs and the symptoms plays a vital part in ensuring that you can make changes to your life in order to live a better way, a healthier, happier way; not a perfect way, but a kinder way. Not all burnout is caused by work. There are thousands of people who work at home caring for children or parents or both; people trying to keep too many balls in the air and not feeling appreciated or acknowledged by those around them.

BURNOUT QUIZ

Below you will find a short quiz from mindtools.com. Take a few minutes to ask yourself the questions to see if you are heading for burnout or already so deeply entrenched in it that it's become your norm.

		Not at all	Rarely	Sometimes	Often	Very often
1	I feel run down and drained of physical or emotional energy					
2	I have negative thoughts about my job					
3	I am harder and less sympathetic with people than perhaps they deserve					
4	I am easily irritated by small problems, or by my co-workers and team					

5	I feel misunderstood or unappreciated by my co–workers					
6	I feel that I have no one to talk to					
7	I feel that I am achieving less than I should					
8	I feel under an unpleasant level of pressure to succeed					
9	I feel that I am not getting what I want out of my job					
10	I feel that I am in the wrong job or organisation					
11	I am frustrated with parts of my job					
12	I feel that work politics frustrate my ability to do a good job					
13	I feel that there is more work to do than I practically can do					
14	I feel that I do not have time to do many of the things that are important to doing a good-quality job					
15	I find that I do not have time to plan as much as I would like					

Calculate your score: score 1 for not at all, 2 for rarely, 3 for sometimes, 4 for often and 5 for very often.

If you score:

15–18	No sign of burnout
19–32	Little sign of burnout; keep an eye on how you feel
33–49	You may be at risk of burnout. Look at ways to re-evaluate your personal and professional goals and adjust accordingly
50–59	You are at risk of burnout. Look at strategies to reduce burnout
60–75	You are at very high risk of burnout

Note: This is by no means a medical validation or diagnosis of burnout. This is purely an informal guide to show you what some of the signs can be. Please consider your mood and anything unexpected that may have happened to you or around you when you complete this test. If you are in any way concerned, see your GP.

Causes of work-related burnout include:

◑ Feeling little or no control over work

◑ Lack of recognition for good performance

◑ Unclear or excessively high job expectations

◑ Monotonous or unchallenging work

◑ Extreme lack of structure and/or high-pressure environment.

Causes of lifestyle-related burnout include:

◑ Not enough time for relaxing and social life

◑ Being expected to be too many things for too many people

◑ Taking on too many responsibilities while others are not helping enough

◑ Insufficient sleep

◑ Lack of close, supportive relationships.

When I was writing this book, I was invited to speak at a conference in Dublin about burnout and how to manage yourself in the workplace. I also gave a workshop to a number of the delegates who worked in office environments. Throughout the workshop a number of attendees broke down and cried at the pressure they were under from their bosses – the pressure to be contactable out of hours, to check emails at weekends and to spend part of their Sundays going online to ensure they were organised for Monday. The habits that had been created were so ingrained that the fear of pushing back and putting boundaries in place seemed utterly daunting.

This may seem over-dramatic, but it was very real for these people; the fear that if they said no to work requests they would be made to feel they were lacking commitment to their jobs clearly showed how easily burnout creeps up and takes over. One particular delegate cried openly about the level of burnout she was experiencing in her job. I met a lady who has been an executive PA for many years in the same company. Her boss retired, and she found herself with a new boss who did things differently and came with her own set of wants, needs and new expectations. Because of these new working conditions, the executive PA was finding she was under constant stress and feeling extremely undervalued in her job. During the workshop, when she shared her story, the other delegates in the room asked her an obvious question: 'Why don't you leave and find another job?' I could see her whole body shake at the thought of this. She had spent the last thirty years working in the company and her self-worth had been directly tied to her job. Not only did she feel she couldn't change jobs, she also felt her age was against her. She felt totally trapped and instead of looking at what she could do for herself to manage the situation, she focused on how trapped she was. All her focus was on how her new boss was impacting on her negatively. After the workshop I spoke to this lady and she subsequently came to see me as a private client. Over a few months we worked through some of tools and exercises I explain in this book and helped her to understand that none of us is in control of other people; we are only in control of how we respond to others' actions. It didn't make her boss less of a tyrant, but it has changed the way this lovely lady views her job. She no longer feels trapped and no longer dreads going to work every day. Yes, she still has bad days, but now she knows how to manage them.

SOME LESS OBVIOUS CAUSES

According to writers and researchers, burnout can also be caused by long-term involvement in situations that are emotionally demanding, such as being a carer, having a hectic family life, or being devoted to a cause, a way of life, or a relationship that has failed to produce the expected reward.

According to the *Maslach Burnout Inventory Manual,* burnout can also be seen as an indicator of the discrepancy between one's character or personal values and one's duties at work. So, for example, a nurse who values patient care and respect who find themselves working an overcrowded A&E department day in and day out, unable to provide the kind of care they think the patients should have, may find that over time this discrepancy leads to burnout.

Certain personality traits can make people more vulnerable to burnout. These include:

- Perfectionism: nothing is ever good enough
- A pessimistic view of oneself and the world
- The need for control – reluctance or inability to delegate
- A high-achieving, type-A personality
- Being introverted or extroverted.

SARAH'S STORY

Sarah is a client who came to see me displaying all the symptoms of burnout. She was utterly exhausted, had no energy after a full night's sleep, was irritable and had no interest in meeting friends socially or even attending family events. Her routine was out of kilter and she felt she was playing catch-up every single day. Everything she did felt like a chore; she described herself as living in a thick fog that slowed down her ability to do anything.

What was really interesting was that she was really happy with her job and therefore didn't think she was suffering from burnout. Sarah had been an employee in large companies all her working life, and a few years earlier she made a huge career change and left the security of being an employee. She took redundancy and set up her own company. She challenged all her limiting self-beliefs and her fear of the unknown, and embarked on following her dream. At the time of all this change, Sarah was married (she still is), had two small children and her mum was living with her, yet she still found the emotional and physical strength to embrace her new venture. She told me she (almost) never regretted the decision to work for herself. Working from home allowed her to adapt her working hours to her children's schedules and although she was now working longer days she was much happier with her new set-up.

She had always felt her youngest child was difficult, but nothing that wasn't normal. Over the next few years she began to find her daughter more and more difficult to manage and by the time she was nine years old she was, Sarah said, 'very simply, a nightmare to be around'. Sarah decided to have her daughter psychologically assessed and was told she had borderline Autistic Spectrum Disorder (ASD) and Attention Deficit Hyperactivity Disorder (ADHD). Rather than seeing this as a negative, Sarah embraced this new information and both she and her husband learned all they could about ASD and ADHD so that they could support their daughter as best they could. By the time Sarah came to see me, her daughter was eleven and causing chaos in the home. She rebelled against family rules and boundaries and pretty much every interaction Sarah had with her resulted in an argument. The continual arguments and unpleasant (to put it mildly) atmosphere was putting huge pressure on Sarah's relationship with her husband and her other daughter. Sarah took all her daughter's behaviour personally and felt that it was her parenting that was wrong.

23

She had gone to parenting classes in order to learn how to manage living with a child with ASD and ADHD, but what she didn't do was look at how important her self-care was in all of this. Her energy focus was split in two: one-half was her work, which she loved and gave her a great sense of fulfilment; the other half was her home, which she began to view as 'toxic'. She dreaded her time with her daughter and found a five-minute interaction left her emotionally and physically drained. The more we discussed this, the more Sarah started to be able to see how the way she was reacting to her daughter was causing her symptoms of burnout.

Sarah had got into the habit of viewing time with her daughter as a battle; her stress hormones were nearly always switched on and increasingly she was taking that feeling with her into her work environment. She had become so exhausted from her daughter's behaviour that she was in a constant state of being reactive rather than responsive.

I quickly identified that Sarah liked to be in control. She was by no means a controlling person, but as she worked for herself and was not answerable to anyone, she was fully in control of how and when she worked. Her home life was pretty similar; she had a very structured routine. She delegated small jobs to the girls and had put systems in place to create order, but her daughter refused to take instructions and would go so far as to do the opposite of what Sarah wanted her to do. Ultimately Sarah felt out of control at home. Once we were able to identify the source of Sarah's burnout (her reactions to her daughter's behaviour) and her own need for control, we began to work out a realistic healthy plan to rebuild her self-care and be able to view her interactions from a healthy responsive place. Sarah had to realise that her daughter did not wake up every morning with the sole purpose of making her mother's life as difficult as possible.

Sarah started to practice mindfulness every morning before she left her bedroom. She focused on her breathing and, using guided ten-minute meditations, started to let go of thinking of her daughter first thing in the morning. Before Sarah left her bedroom to 'face the music', as she put it, she would write down three things she was grateful for in her life. Initially she struggled with thinking of even one, but now she is in the habit she easily finds things to be grateful for. She started practising a two-minute breathing exercise whenever she felt she was getting sucked into her daughter's behaviour. She learned not to take things personally. She learned to be kind to herself and value her self-care. Over the course of a few months Sarah changed from feeling as though she didn't care any more to caring more than ever.

And no, her daughter's behaviour didn't change drastically overnight, although it did improve. The cycle of toxic emotions at home reduced dramatically, Sarah had more physical energy to get back into going for walks; she had more emotional energy to see her friends; and her relationships with her other family members got better.

Sarah still comes to see me once a month for, as she calls it, her 'monthly self-care check-in'. She recognises she can't change other people's behaviour, but she does have control over how she manages her own.

IS CHANGING JOBS THE SOLUTION?

> 'The only Zen you'll find on mountain tops is the Zen you bring up there with you.' Alan Watts

If your job is the main source of your stress and burnout, it may seem that the most obvious option is simply to change your job. The desire to run away and the belief that a different job will magically change all your problems might work, or it may be that all you'll end up doing is bringing the problems with you. It may be that changing jobs may not even be an option – your age, the job market, your specialised area of work or even location could mean that you have no choice but to stay where you are.

Whether or not you have the option of jumping ship and changing careers, it's worthwhile to figure out new ways to improve your current situation in the now before you decide to change jobs. The reality is that if you don't address what's happening to you in your current situation, there's a big chance your feelings and reactions will follow you to your next job. You might think that a dramatic career change will improve everything. But it can't. Only you can.

If, for example, working with the mindset of being a perfectionist is something you currently do, and this is contributing or has contributed to you being burnt-out and you haven't addressed how to manage how it affects you and your work, moving jobs will only mean you're going to end up repeating the same behavioural patterns.

Before you think changing job is the answer to your burnout, take a moment to see what's really going on for you. Maybe you need to change your behaviours before you change your job. You can't run away from yourself.

JANE'S STORY

Like Jane, I believed I could run away from my experiences of being burnt-out by not only moving jobs, but by moving countries (for me it was repeatedly).

Jane first came to see me shortly after having moved to Dublin from Oman. Although she was born in Oman, her mother was Irish, she had spent all her summer holidays in Ireland, and Ireland was like her second home; so it seemed like an obvious choice when she experienced burnout in her job and her relationship back in Oman.

Rather than addressing what internal factors may have caused her to reach burnout, she rationalised that moving countries, changing jobs and starting a whole new way of life would be the answer to her situation. It took approximately six months of living and working in Dublin for her to realise that not one single symptom of her burnout had dissipated. She was, in fact, more burnt-out than when she left Oman. She had added the stress of moving jobs and countries to her life and felt more out of control than ever. Jane had tried to run away from herself without realising that maybe she needed to address how she dealt with life and change her behaviours in order to be able to respond rather than react to situations.

It became apparent that Jane was struggling with the belief system she had grown up with and her current belief system. Jane was the daughter of an Irish mother and an Omani father, her faith and culture was Muslim, yet she spent her summers in Ireland, and with that came a freedom she didn't have in Oman. As she reached her late teens, it became increasingly harder for her to conform to the strict beliefs and rules that came with being a Muslim girl in a Muslim country. By the time she entered her twenties, her core values and new belief system didn't align with the one she was raised with and still lived with. Living your life being incongruent to your core values is a major factor in becoming burnt-out.

Jane thought that by moving countries she could automatically change how she felt. But her childhood value system was so deeply ingrained in her that rather than leaving behind how she felt in Oman, she ended up bringing all her stresses, guilt and limiting self-beliefs with her. She was now burnt-out in another country with little or no support system. In fact, she changed jobs quite a few times over a two-year period; she would blame the job or the people for her stress and burnout.

It wasn't until Jane started to understand how her current core values conflicted with her childhood values that she could begin living her life being utterly congruent to how she felt now. She started to realise that unless she addressed her own limiting self-beliefs and other behavioural patterns, she wasn't going to feel any different, wherever she worked or lived. Yes, taking personal responsibility for your own actions can be hard, but, believe me, the rewards are worth it!

WHEN CHANGING JOBS ISN'T AN OPTION

This book gets you to look at areas of your life that have been affected by burnout and gives suggestions and advice on how to recover from or prevent burnout. This bit of advice is about what you can practically and proactively do in your current job when you think changing jobs is the only solution to being burnt-out, yet circumstances don't allow you to do it.

- **Check your job description.** If work overload is an issue for you, get a copy of your job description and use it as a template to create a second one that lists what you're actually doing now. A lot of job descriptions (I'd say most of them) are not updated when roles and responsibilities change. Compare the two and share it with your manager or, if appropriate, your HR department, and ask them to update the description of your job and responsibilities. Be proactive and point out things you've been expected to do that are not part of your job description or are not being acknowledged, and that may be contributing to your burnout. Let the powers that be know that you are overstretched. Doing a job description comparison allows you to remove yourself from being emotional and addresses the situation from a place of facts.

- **Solution focus.** Now that you have a job description comparison in black and white, use it proactively. Decide what it is that you need to happen within your role in order for you to (a) feel less stress and (b) feel more appreciated. If you're burnt-out and hate your job, proposing a solution to the problem rather than just looking at the problem can sometimes make a difference. It is amazing how many companies, small or large, are so busy that they don't have time to figure out solutions to what could be relatively small issues that stack up and become raging infernos. You identifying the problem that is contributing to your burnout *and* suggesting a solution could make a difference.

- **Use the tool kit.** Take a deep breath and start implementing the tools in this book to recover and recharge from burnout. Take this opportunity to learn how your behaviours have impacted you negatively in how you work, and work on changing them for the better.

Of course, changing job may be the answer to ultimately ensuring that you don't experience burnout again – maybe even a complete change of job or career is what you need – but before you start thinking that this will be the answer to how you feel, make the positive changes you really need, and start today.

Week 3

Stress: internal and external stressors

Weeks 1 and 2 have been about getting to understand the term burnout, identifying possible causes and hopefully getting you to realise that you are not alone in the symptoms you may be experiencing. This week I explain exactly what stress is, how it impacts your body and mind, how situations outside your control (external stressors), your personality type, how you think, feel and react to the world (internal stressors) can cause high levels of negative stress, which can then lead to burnout. Knowing what stress actually is and how you need good stress in order to survive and function is important to make changes in your life.

WHAT IS STRESS?

Stress isn't always bad. In small doses, it can help you perform under pressure and motivate you to do your best. Think of football players – the level of stress in their bodies prior to a big match is what motivates them to get on the pitch and kick ass. The body is an utterly amazing thing and the stress response is your body's way of protecting you. It works to help you stay focused, energetic and alert. In emergency situations, stress and the way you respond to it can save your life; stress gives you extra strength to defend yourself. For example, the stress response is what makes you slam on the brakes of your car if someone runs out in front of you. A good example is how our caveman ancestors responded to stress. The cavemen are out hunting for food and stumble on a vicious animal. They can either kill it for food or run away from it because it could kill them. This is a high-stress situation and their stress levels automatically increase dramatically. Their hearts are pounding, they breathe faster, all their senses are suddenly much sharper in order to deal with the situation. Their bodies, now in a heightened state of response, are in the fight-or-flight stress response. They can use their increased stress hormones to either fight the animal or flee the dangerous situation. Both reactions are the results of stress and neither is wrong. What's important to understand is that whether they choose to fight or flee, once they have either killed the animal or run away from it, they are now out of the stressful situation and their stress hormones will return to normal. They are not living in a constant state of stress.

Stress can also help you rise to meet challenges. A healthy level of stress is what keeps you on your toes during a presentation at work or college, it's what focuses your concentration when you're participating in a team sport or drives you to study for an exam when you'd rather be watching TV.

It's only when stress becomes a continual part of your everyday living, or when you feel you're not in control of a situation, that it negatively affects you and can lead to burnout.

Here, then, are four reasons you should rest easier when it comes to every day stress – and how a little short-term stress can actually benefit your brain and body.

- **It helps boost brainpower (in short bursts).** This is a bit of a biology lesson, but I think it's important to understand what exactly happens to your body when you're experiencing short bursts of stress.

Low-level stress stimulates the production of brain chemicals called neurotrophins and strengthens the connections between neurons in the brain. Neurons are nerve cells that are the basic building block of our nervous system, and their job is to transmit information throughout our body. It is thought that the production of the chemical neurotrophin, also produced by exercise (a physical stressor) can help boost productivity and concentration. Yet another reason why exercise is good for you!

- **It can increase immunity – in the short term.** When your body is responding to stress, it is also preparing itself for the possibility of being injured or the risk of infection. It does this is by producing extra interleukins (these are molecules that are not regularly produced in the body but fire into action when the body is under stress) that help regulate the immune system, providing at least a temporary defensive mechanism to ward off oncoming infection.

- **It can make you more resilient.** Learning to deal with stressful situations can make future ones easier to manage and can even help normalise situations and events that had previously been stressful for you. An extreme example of this is idea behind the US Navy SEAL training. I don't expect anyone to put themselves through this level of stress to improve their resilience – it's an example to show you how learning to deal with stressful situations can help you with future stressful situations – you can benefit from less extreme experiences too. The SEALs is an elite response unit subjected to extreme stressful situations in their line of duty. In their training, they are repeatedly exposed to stressful events, giving their bodies the chance to develop both a physical and psychological sense of control, so when they are in real-life combat, their bodies don't shut down due to fear and stress. They learn to use their stress to make them more resilient and better able to deal with future stressful situations.

○ **It motivates you to succeed.** Good stress – the scientific word for this is eustress – can motivate you to get a job done. The key in this thought is to view stressful situations as a challenge that you can meet, rather than an overwhelming brick wall you can't knock down.

So a healthy level of stress in your life is good for you. Living in a constant state of stress is not.

> To sum up: the stress responses in our body are perfectly normal and are vital to basic survival. Stress can be physical or psychological, it is important for healthy bodies and minds, and can be triggered by both pleasant and unpleasant things. Stress needs to be released, and rest and recuperation is required for your body to recover properly.

HOW CAN STRESS LEAD TO BURNOUT?

As we've seen, stress (in short bursts) can have a positive impact on our physical and emotional wellbeing, but too much has the opposite effect. Stress is one of those words that we try to run away from because it conjures up negative thoughts of over-work and generally not being able to cope. For some, acknowledging or thinking that they can't cope is a huge stressor in itself. However, we need to realise that we do actually require a certain level of stress in order to function in our day-to-day lives. We also have to understand that asking for help is not a sign of not coping; it is a sign that we would benefit from a bit of help.

But when we're constantly running in emergency mode – you know the feeling – when everything you do seems as stressful as the last thing, when even doing the food shop is stressful, our minds and bodies pay the price. If you regularly find yourself feeling stressed out and overwhelmed, it's time to take action to bring your nervous system back into balance. And now here's the really good part: you can take charge of yourself, improve how you think and feel, learn how to recognise the signs and symptoms of chronic stress and take steps to reduce its harmful effects.

We saw earlier that stress is our body's way of responding to any kind of demand or threat – remember the cavemen? Even though we have evolved enormously since those days, when we sense danger or are confronted with a stressful situation, real or imagined, the body's automatic defence mechanism still kicks into a rapid, automatic process known as the fight-or-flight reaction or the stress response. This happens automatically and without thinking. So when you feel threatened, the body's nervous system jumps into high-alert mode and responds by releasing a load of stress hormones such as adrenaline and cortisol, which signal to the body that there is an emergency and action is needed ASAP. You'll know the feeling: your heartbeat increases, your muscles tighten, your breathing quickens, your blood pressure rises (though you're not aware of it), and all your senses suddenly become sharper. All of these physical reactions come together to increase your ability to cope with danger, in essence to get you ready to either fight or flee the situation.

> Stress is like a boiling pot: when it starts to boil over, stress stops being helpful and starts causing major damage to your health, your mood, your productivity, your relationships and your quality of life.

One of the downsides of stress is that your nervous system isn't very good at recognising the difference between emotional and physical threats. If you're stressed over an argument with a friend, a work deadline, unpaid bills, breaking up with a partner, or if you're just not very good at healthy confrontation, your body can react just as strongly as if you're facing a truly life-or-death situation. The more your emergency stress system is stimulated, the easier it becomes to trigger and the harder it becomes to get yourself back to feeling calm again.

If you find you're getting stressed out regularly, your body may be in a heightened state of stress most of the time. And that can lead to health problems affecting your immune system and your organs. It can also rewire the brain, leaving you more vulnerable to anxiety, depression and other mental health problems.

Earlier I used the analogy of the light bulb: if you leave it switched on, it will eventually overheat and it might blow. When we experience a stress situation, we 'switch on', but when the stressor passes, our internal light bulb turns off, allowing the body to recharge, the heart rate and breathing to return to normal. With chronic stress the light bulb does not switch off and the body is in a heightened state of stress, releasing cortisol and putting continual stress on the body.

The most dangerous thing about stress (and burnout) is how easily it creeps up on you. Because of the 'busyness' of life and the fact that everyone else seems to be stressed, you don't want to show that you 'can't cope'. You try to manage it yourself and before you know it, it starts to feel familiar, even normal. That's why it's important to be aware of the common warning signs and symptoms of when stress is becoming a daily occurrence and what you can do to manage it best for you.

The situations and pressures in life that can cause stress are known as stressors. And while I've primarily talked about negative stressors, anything that puts high demands on you can be stressful, including positive events such as getting married, buying a house, going to college, receiving a promotion or moving to another country.

And just to add to all of this, not all stress is caused by *external* factors. Stress can also be internal or self-generated, when you worry too much about something that may or may not happen, have irrational, pessimistic thoughts about life or place demanding expectations on yourself.

Finally, what causes stress depends, at least in part, on your perception of it. Something that's stressful to you may not faze someone else; they may even enjoy it. For example, your morning journey to work may make you anxious and tense because you worry that traffic will make you late. Others, however, may find the trip relaxing because they allow more than enough time and enjoy listening to music while they drive or sit on the train or bus.

Here is a list of some external and internal causes of stress. Can you identify with any of them?

Common external causes of stress	Common internal causes of stress
Major life changes	Pessimism
Work or school	Inability to accept uncertainty
Relationship difficulties	Rigid thinking, lack of flexibility
Financial problems	Negative self-talk
Being too busy	Unrealistic expectations/ perfectionism
Children and family	All-or-nothing attitude

CIARAN'S STORY

Ciaran is one of only two men I talk about in this book, not because I don't work wih men in my practice, but because I think men are more inclined not to admit when they are continually stressed and heading towards burnout. In my experience (and it is by no means fact-based!) they seem to view it as a sign of weakness and this only adds to the negative feelings they already have.

Ciaran initially called to make an appointment to see me with his wife. In one of those bizarre serendipitous moments they had both been driving separately, listening to the radio, and heard me being interviewed about burnout and the effects it can have not just on the individual but on families too. Ciaran and his wife were recently married and had a young baby and were feeling the pressures of having successful careers and a new baby in their lives. In essence their relationship was good; they just needed reassurance that they were doing great and the acknowledgement that having a new baby demands a period of adjustment.

At the joint session Ciaran explained to me that earlier in the year, while lying on the sofa watching TV, he suddenly felt his chest tighten and couldn't breathe. He genuinely thought he was having a heart attack. He called an ambulance (his wife was away) and was admitted overnight for tests. All his results and tests came back clear. He was a healthy 31-year-old man who was not having a heart attack. His body was responding to the effects of extreme stress and was screaming out for attention and care. Interestingly, Ciaran's health scare didn't happen while he was in the middle of a stressful situation at work, but rather when he was at home and least expecting it. While his body was trying to relax, it was in constant battle with his stress levels which resulted in a form of a panic attack.

Ciaran's story is one I've always been drawn to. He is the first person in his extended family to finish school and go on to college, where he studied law. He broke the mould of his family; he could have ended up on the wrong side of the tracks, but he used his upbringing to motivate him to break the cycle of his family history. Ciaran used all the limiting self-beliefs he had been told and believed as a child as his driver to be successful. By the time I met him he was well on the way to being made a partner in a large, well-respected law firm.

All too often I see clients who live their lives by the rule of thumb of 'when I just achieve X, I'll slow down' or 'I have to work this hard' and the negative effect of this way of thinking is knowing when 'enough' is actually 'enough'. With this way of thinking it's easy to keep extending your personal goalposts until it becomes difficult to let go and be comfortable with what you have achieved. For Ciaran his level of achievement was coming at a price and his self-care had not only taken a back seat, it had been kicked to the kerb. Life had become a cycle of early mornings to get work done, long days with clients or in court, late nights catching up on paperwork, regular weekends of being on call and trying to spend time with his family. It wasn't leaving a whole lot of time for his self-care.

When Ciaran came to see me he had trouble sleeping, wasn't exercising, was eating poorly, was constantly thinking about work and had forgotten how to be present in the now. His lack of sleep impacted his waking hours and was putting untold amounts of stress on his young body. If he continued like this he would probably have ended up in hospital for longer than the 24 hours he had already spent there, as the body cannot sustain this level of stress.

Ciaran already had an understanding of what being kind to himself meant; he just wasn't living it. The connection between knowing what he needed to do and actually doing it had been broken. As a young teenager he played sport, which he continued at college, and even though he socialised, studied and did all the normal college things a young twenty-something does, his life wasn't as busy as it is now. After college Ciaran worked for a while in his home town, but a few years later he was offered a job in another city, which involved moving (with his new wife), and with that his self-care took a nose dive. He stopped playing sport and replaced it with sitting at a desk or in his car, which also meant that he lost the weekly social connection of the friends he played with. Finding the time to join a new GAA club was not on his list of non-negotiables. Without realising, he had lost any free time for meeting friends and switching off.

Ciaran's work involves a certain amount of socialising and networking at lunches, dinners and evening functions, which was also taking its toll on him. He was now spending his time working, trying to spend time with his wife or travelling back home to visit his extended family. On some levels Ciaran's later story isn't unique – we all experience change when we leave the comfort of college life – but the part I want to share is how easy it is to get caught up in the treadmill of life, which sometimes just gets faster, and faster which results in us not knowing how to slow down or reclaim time for self-care.

Ciaran couldn't see how he was going to magically create time each day or even every week to start practising self-care.

Ciaran and I examined how his average day unfolds. There will always be unexpected events, but even allowing for them makes a difference, and we were able to start seeing where he could start to make changes to his behaviours. Ciaran really missed playing sports and although he wasn't in a position right away to start going to a new club, we looked at a practical way he could bring exercise into his day without taking up huge amounts of time, which he didn't have anyway. Previously he had always driven to work, as he might have to drive to visit a client at a moment's notice, so his car had to be available. He would also use this opportunity to make work calls and therefore was starting his working day even earlier than he thought. He mentioned that he had a bicycle, which he rarely had time to use. Ciaran has secure parking at work, so I suggested he cycle to and from work while leaving his car at the office should he need it. This one simple change has made a big difference. Not only does he start each day with some physical activity, his body is releasing all the positive hormones exercise promotes, he is not on his phone making calls and, without even being aware of it, he was now starting to practise mindfulness – cycling in a busy city centre requires your full attention. As a side note, because he is getting some physical activity back into his life, his sleeping has improved too. One of the other areas Ciaran was able to implement in his life was counterbalance, which I explain in Week 6, to offset the busy periods of work in his life. He recently took a two-week holiday with his family, turned off his phone and spent the time being fully present in the here and now.

Ciaran still works extremely hard; however, he has learned how important his self-care is in order to attain his professional goals. He cycles to work whenever he can, goes swimming with his young daughter, knows when his sleep needs attention and schedules in time to attend sessions with me. Ciaran was always aware of what he needed to do to nurture his self-care; he just needed guidance in how to implement it to suit his lifestyle in order to prevent burnout.

INTERNAL STRESS

Internal stress comes from inside us and determines our body's ability to respond to, and deal with, the external stressors we are facing. I've listed some of them here, but it's important to remember that on different days your internal wellbeing and ability to deal with different levels of stress will change. If you are persistently ignoring these areas of your life, you are not caring for yourself – in other words, your self-care needs attention!

- **Nutrition.** How you eat and what you eat. As the saying goes, 'you are what you eat'. If you are missing meals, eating more processed foods than good home-cooked meals and thinking that five cups of coffee equals your daily water intake, you may need to look at how you could change your nutritional habits. Every small change adds up to a bigger bank of resilience that works at keeping burnout at bay.

- **Thoughts.** The way you think affects the way you feel and the way you behave. If your thoughts are based on a 'what if' rather than a fact, it can have a negative impact on how your feel and in turn cause you to behave in a way that is not beneficial to you in the slightest. This wheel of thought-feeling–behaviour based on no facts can create a huge internal stress and lead to feelings of anxiety too.

- **Feelings of anger, fear and worry.** All of these feelings cause stress on our bodies. They can be caused by external factors, but they can also be caused by the internal wheel of thought–feeling–behaviour. Understanding exactly why you are angry, fearful or worried can allow you to break the situation down. More often than not we are not actually angry at what we think we are.

- **Anticipation.** The anticipation that something bad is going to happen or expecting the worst in any given situation will cause stress internally. Equally, if you are someone who hates surprises and know your family and friends are throwing a surprise party for you, your level of anticipation may be coupled with worry and fear, which will impact your stress levels if you are not minding your self-care.

- **Memory.** Often we link current events, or even future events, with past memories that may have been upsetting or difficult. A memory is exactly that; a memory, an event that happened in the past. Learning how to detach the emotion from the memory allows you to enjoy the current or future event without feeling stressed.

- **Recurring illness.** When your body is under stress for prolonged periods of time, it gets run down physically. Recurring colds, sinus infections, headaches and other minor illnesses feed off stress. More worryingly, a huge number of people are stressed because of fear of a major illness yet are too fearful to visit their doctor to confirm or dismiss their concerns. Bite the bullet and get checked by your doctor immediately!

- **Emotional wellbeing.** This is so important and I talk about it over and over. If you are not emotionally healthy, your body won't be either. I'll discuss this a lot more in later chapters. In the meantime think about what you could do for yourself every day to nourish your emotional wellbeing.

- **Sleep and rest.** I am passionate, truly, utterly passionate, about sleep. I've dedicated a whole section to sleep, the reason we need it, what it does to promote a healthy body and what happens when we are consistently sleep-deprived. Sleep does not make external stressors magically disappear, but it does make them a hell of a lot easier to manage.

EXTERNAL STRESS

External stress and stressors come from outside us. Some stressors we have no obvious control over; others we can either control or learn new ways of managing them that don't impact us negatively. External stressors can be:

- **Your job.** Having a job with too much to do and not enough hours in the day to achieve it all. Constant interruptions in your working day from colleagues and bosses. Getting into the habit of checking emails regularly both in and out of the office. Does all this sound familiar?

- **Your working conditions.** Add to that a stressful working environment. If you are someone who needs to work in silence and your office is open-plan, that would be a constant background stressor impacting on you emotionally and physically. If your job requires you to drive regularly, this could also be a stressor you have no control over – the constant traffic and dealing with other people's driving habits. What if you could put yourself in the other person's shoes and realise that they, too, may be having a bad day?

- **Trauma and/or injury.** An unexpected trauma such as a bereavement, separation or perhaps an unexpected redundancy can contribute to your body responding on high alert. Even an injury that leaves you unable to carry out your daily tasks for a short period of time can cause stress.

- **Relationships.** We often think that family members, or friends we have chosen to be with, shouldn't cause us stress. All relationships at some point cause us stress! The important thing to remember is how you manage yourself in relationships. Are you prone to putting others first at the detriment of yourself? Are you staying attached to friendships out of a sense of duty even if the relationship is toxic and not healthy? Surrounding yourself with people who have similar values and beliefs affects how you feel. Toxic relationships equals stress, always.

- **Our physical environment.** I talk about this later in the book, but for now, think about the environment you live in. If it is cluttered, loud and chaotic, and you are not ensuring your self-care is high up on your priority list, the chances are that your physical environment is adding to your stress.

Add to these all the miscellaneous situations, challenges, difficulties and expectations we're confronted with on a daily basis that come with the hectic lives we live, and a recipe for burnout is stewing away in the background. This is why learning how to prioritise your self-care is not just important but essential.

Personally, one of my biggest stressors is being a **parent** and I openly speak about the challenges that my darling boys throw at me everyday. For those of you who are parents, here are few tips on how to manage yourself when you're managing them!

- Understand that these little people came into your life with their own map of the world. They have their own opinions, values and way of looking at situations, which might not be the same as yours, but they have a voice.

- Accept your kids for who and what they are.

- Realise that you're human and your kids know it. Trying to be a perfect parent is hugely stressful and time-consuming. And inevitably, if you're working really hard at being a perfect parent, you might just miss out on them growing up. Be the best you can on any given day and ask for help!

➡ Children are like sponges. If they see you stressed, angry, sad, tired or irritable, chances are they will learn to imitate you and take on your stresses. Learn to laugh at the small stuff and remember we're all still learning.

➡ As a single parent I struggled with the difference between authoritarian parenting (there are many definitions of this style of parenting, but in short it is based on the theory that children should be punished without explanation when the high standards set have not been met or children refuse to do as they are told) and authoritative parenting, which, although it is also about setting boundaries and rules, is much more compassionate and works at teaching children to take personal responsibility. In case you're wondering, I didn't actually know the difference. I felt that these little people were living in my world and should therefore do as I said. I didn't feel I needed – or had the time – to explain why I was asking the boys to adhere to my rules. That, I learned, does not work. It added to my stress that they wouldn't comply! Children respond to authoritative parenting. They like boundaries (even if they say they don't), because they make them feel safe. Parenting is not about control. It's about freedom and doing the job with as little stress as possible.

We all need a healthy level of stress in our lives to be able to react quickly and efficiently. Stress can affect us both internally and externally. Being in a constant state of stress can lead to burnout. Burnout does not happen overnight and is a build-up of numerous factors.

ADRENAL FATIGUE

Adrenal fatigue is the result of living in a state of constant stress whereby your adrenal glands do not get a chance to recover from continually producing cortisol. Interestingly enough, although adrenal fatigue is recognised in some areas of health and alternative medical practices as a condition relating to chronic stress and burnout, it is currently not accepted as a medical diagnosis.

Typical causes of adrenal fatigue include long-term stress and burnout from jobs, relationship problems or even living with a chronic illness. If continual pressure is put on the adrenal glands, they can weaken to the point that they are unable to respond efficiently when we need them most. People suffering from adrenal fatigue will complain of symptoms like constant tiredness, having a lack of enthusiasm and even mild depression. Even sleeping for long periods of time doesn't help; they wake up just as tired as when they went to bed.

Adrenal fatigue was first identified in the 1930s by Dr Hans Selye. He proved that chronic stress leads to exhaustion, which with our modern pace of living can also be identified as a symptom of burnout.

These are only some symptoms you may experience if you are suffering from adrenal fatigue:

- mild depression or anxiety
- multiple food allergies
- lethargy and lack of energy
- increased effort to perform daily tasks
- decreased ability to handle stress
- dry and thin skin
- low blood sugar
- low body temperature.

I would stress that if you are experiencing any of these symptoms and are concerned about your health, make an appointment with your GP. Your health is your responsibility and while a lot of the symptoms of adrenal fatigue are treatable with a lifestyle overhaul, it is vital that you rule out any other conditions first.

Much of the recovery of adrenal fatigue centres on nutrition, which is why I've dedicated a whole section to the benefits of healthy eating (see Week 5). Along with your nutrition, good sleep, gentle exercise and lots of rest is recommended to aid you in your recovery.

TEND-AND-BEFRIEND

There is an interesting stress response that is seems to be unique to women and highlights the importance for women of a good social structure of friends. The 'tend-and-befriend' response is different from the fight-or-flight response to stress, which is common to both men and women. In times of stress women not only release cortisol but also the hormone oxytocin, the hormone often associated with caregiving, labour and the attachment between mothers and babies. Oxytocin also creates a feeling of relaxation and helps to reduce feelings of fear. Men also produce oxytocin, but their testosterone decreases their oxytocin levels and so men fail to benefit from the calming effects oxytocin releases.

So what is the difference between fight-or-flight and tend-and-befriend? Well, tend-and-befriend has been found to be a direct response to how women react when they feel their children are under threat. Like the fight-or-flight response, it can be traced back to our early ancestors. In tend-and-befriend, a woman will want to tend to her family and will befriend others to help her survive. Just like fight-or-flight, the response is not a conscious reaction and is embedded deep in our being.

Think back to our cavemen example. The men are out hunting for food and the women stay in the village to care for the children and hold the fort. Here's an interesting thing – the women are also experiencing stress.

Will the men return from the hunt with food? Will they be killed? Will a starving lion attack the village while the men are way? And if so, who will protect their children? This type of stress causes the tend-and-befriend response to kick in and it's what drives the women to befriend other village mothers. If a starving lion attacks, the mother has to defend her children, and if she herself is killed, she needs to know that she has befriended other mothers who will tend to her children.

Research has shown that women with strong social connections have an improved quality of life, lower blood pressure and cholesterol levels. Women naturally seek each other for comfort when stressed. Having a good friend (in work, personally or at a group) when you are stressed can enable the release of additional oxytocin, which can help create a greater sense of calm. Not only can female friends offer emotional support, but the research shows that their comfort provides health benefits as well. If you are unable to make social connections, for whatever reason, whether you're a new mum, feeling isolated in work, a stay-at-home mum or have recently moved countries, look at reconnecting socially with others. Use the tend-and-befriend instinct.

HOW TO TURN BAD STRESS INTO A GOOD SITUATION

There are many ways you can turn bad stress into good, productive, stress. Once you have identified what your stressors are and where they are originating from, you can learn to use them (or at least some of them) as motivators and how to view stress differently.

Start by making a list of all your stressors.

- Where is your stress coming from? Is it from work or home? Take time to really identify what exactly your stressors are. It's all too easy to say, 'I'm really stressed right now', but not actually know what it is that is causing you to feel stressed. Think about your 'background' stressors, the ones that linger off-stage all the time, such as a bad relationship, a tricky friendship or constantly feeling unwell. Write in your journal a list of all the stressors you have identified and where they come from.

➡ Now the challenging bit – identify and include your good stressors. This could include getting excited about a wedding, sports game, a public speaking event, a presentation or challenging project at work that pushes you outside your comfort zone.

➡ Write down how each stressor makes you feel. Can you put into words what the stress in your body feels like? What thoughts do you have when you think about both your good and bad stressors? Doing this helps you establish which stressors are good or bad, and gives you a starting point for changing how you feel and react to them. By doing the above exercise you can start to figure out what stressors are created by no fault or action of your own; in other words, they are out of your control. These are the ones you'll have to learn how to respond differently to. Stressors created by your own actions are more easily resolved as you're in control of them and can work through how to minimise or remove them.

➡ Learn to let stress act as a warning sign. By viewing stress as a warning sign (rather than as something to panic about or let control you), you'll be able to let your stress act as a motivator. If your stress is work-related, try to identify the source of it. Remember, your stress is just a sign that your subconscious is preoccupied with a new problem and that your limiting self-beliefs are playing with your mind making you doubt yourself. Tell yourself that the stressed feeling is simply a reminder to be aware of how you feel. It is not a measure of your capabilities in doing your job. Use this stress as a positive motivator to tackle your project and keep asking yourself,

'Why am I feeling stressed?' Once you know exactly what is making you feel stressed, it is easier to rationalise how you feel.

● Change your mindset. One great way to turn negative stress into positive stress is to see situations and events that stress you as challenges to overcome. See stress as an opportunity to change and improve your life. For example, if you get stressed because you didn't get a job you applied for, see it as an opportunity to improve your interview skills rather than letting yourself slip into thinking (a) you're not good enough or (b) creating an ever-bigger feeling of stress for the next interview.

Use your journal to list your bad stressors and identify where they originate from. Also list your good stressors! Work out which stressors are within your control and which ones aren't. Use the signs of negative stress to up your self-care game. Change your mindset to create change in your responses.

Week 4

How your personality contributes to burnout

N ow that you've worked through the first three weeks and have a greater awareness of burnout, the following weeks are where the good work begins.

Week 4 is about delving deeper into who you are, looking at how limiting self-beliefs you may have grown up with or adopted into your life can damage your ability to cope in the world. I explain how your personality type could also be a major contributing element to your burnout. Having a better understanding of your personality type, whether you lean towards being a perfectionist in your approach to home or work life, or are a more introverted than extroverted person, gives you a better understanding of who you are and how your interactions with the world could be impacting on you negatively. This week also looks at the concept of fear of change; what might be holding you back from making the changes that you know you'd like to implement but are too scared to put into action. Week 4 can be challenging; it really gets you to be honest with yourself, as no one else can know who you are as well as you do, so take your time working through it and understand that understanding who you are and what drives you allows you to accept who you are and make changes for the better.

It is not a criticism of who you are. Knowing ourselves, our fears and what might be holding us back creates the opportunity to nurture self-care to protect ourselves from burnout.

LIMITING SELF-BELIEFS

'If you accept a limiting belief, then it will become a truth for you.' **Louise Hay**

I am going to try to explain this as simply as possible as it is really important. In order to change our limiting self-beliefs, we need to understand what they are and how we can overcome them.

Limiting self-beliefs are beliefs you have about yourself and about others that limit how you live your life. We are born with no limiting self-beliefs – as babies we explore without a care in the world and we don't really have anyone to compare ourselves to.

As we get older, start school and make friends, we begin to compare ourselves to others and lose sight of who exactly we are. When explaining where limiting self-beliefs come from, I often use the example of the little boy who loved to climb trees.

This little boy was curious and loved exploring. Every day he would stop at the park with his mother on the way home from school and would run off to climb trees. His mother, although nervous that her son might hurt himself if he fell from high up, always encouraged him and praised his efforts. One week she couldn't collect him, so his dad became his park buddy. When his father saw him climbing trees he shouted at him, 'Don't do that, you might fall and hurt yourself!' and 'Be careful!' and 'You're too young to do that!' By the end of the week the little boy didn't want to climb the trees any more and the following week when his mother took him back to the park the little boy just looked at the trees and didn't attempt to climb them. When his mum asked what was wrong, the little boy said, 'Dad said I can't climb trees because I'm too little and I'll hurt myself.'

In a short space of time, a limiting self-belief was created in the little boy's mind, something that would stay with him for a long time. It was created by a dad out of concern for his son and not intended to be hurtful. However, it is easy to see how telling someone they are not good at something can impact on their lives. The little boy was good at climbing trees, but a few comments about his capabilities was enough to make him believe he wasn't good at climbing.

Limiting self-beliefs may start when we are young, but they can be imposed by others or by ourselves at any stage of our lives. Parents, teachers, siblings, other family members, spouses, work colleagues and bosses can all challenge our self-beliefs by either reinforcing our own negative beliefs or creating new ones.

I was once told by a boss that if I did a secretarial course, I would be an 'all right' secretary. I was 20 years old at the time, nervous, and to this day I've never forgotten those words. They formed the glass layer of my own limiting self-beliefs which I still work at shattering.

These are a few common limiting self-beliefs:

- I'm not very good at my job.
- My sibling(s) is/are much more successful than I am.
- I am not attractive enough to be in a relationship.
- I'm not very intelligent.
- I believe men/women are all liars in relationships.
- I'll never be successful.
- I'll never amount to anything.
- I'm no good so I'll never be promoted.

The really interesting thing about limiting self-beliefs is that most of the time they are so deeply buried in our being that we don't know they're there. We can't remember a time when we didn't have these beliefs, even though we weren't born with them; they have become our norm, the script we play out in life. I often hear clients say, 'That's just the way life is' or, 'There's no point asking for a raise, I just won't get it.' Somewhere along the way of life these thoughts have become their self-beliefs, negative patterns of thoughts and behaviours that paralyse them from making changes.

If you feel your limiting self-beliefs are contributing to symptoms of burnout, ask yourself:

- How did I get here?
- Could my limiting beliefs about myself and/or my world play a part in where I am in life?
- Could my limiting self-beliefs be holding me back from making changes personally and professionally that would serve me better?

FINDING YOUR LIMITING SELF-BELIEFS

How do you discover what your limiting self-beliefs actually are?

In order to challenge and change a belief, it's a good idea to see what patterns of behaviour you repeat that may be holding you back from letting life happen to you rather than living it to your best.

For me, and when I'm working with clients, I get them to write down their limiting self-beliefs. For example:

- My boss thinks I'm no good at my job.
- I was always told in school I wasn't very bright.

● Nobody will ever find me attractive.

● I won't get another job.

Thoughts like these can get in the way of you thinking clearly, can hinder self-care and contribute to burnout. It's self-imposed thoughts, *your* thoughts, that can keep you from making changes. So, your limiting self-beliefs can be responsible for keeping you in a state of negativity and hold you back from taking charge of your life.

ADJUSTING YOUR LIMITING SELF-BELIEFS

Now that you are starting to understand what limiting self-beliefs are and how they impact on you and your world, it's time to start challenging those thoughts. Let's start by breaking your beliefs into different categories.

Existing Relationship Beliefs	New Relationship Beliefs
I should put others first	I will put myself first
I am not good at …	I am good at …
I am scared of failure	I am excited to try something new
I have no time for myself	I am making time for myself
I feel guilty if I do something for myself	I love doing things for myself
Existing Work Beliefs	**New Work Beliefs**
Work must be hard	I enjoy my work
I'll never make enough money doing something I love	I believe I can work at doing something I love
I have to work for as long as it takes to get everything finished	I enjoy setting boundaries and asking for help to get my work finished
My work has to be perfect	I enjoy doing my work well
Work is the most important thing	Work is a part of my life that I enjoy

Existing Money Beliefs	New Money Beliefs
I shouldn't talk about money	It's good to talk about money (we need it)
Money is the root of all evil	Money allows me to do things I enjoy
Money doesn't make you happy	Doing things I enjoy makes me happy
I don't deserve to earn a lot of money	I deserve to earn money
I must work long hours to make money	Working well is better than working hard
Existing Health Beliefs	**New Health Beliefs**
I am always tired	I am practising self-care to look after my body and mind
I don't have time/money/energy to exercise	I allow time in my day to exercise without guilt
Drinking alcohol relaxes me and helps me sleep	I use mindfulness in my day to help me relax and sleep
I cannot call in sick	I listen to my body when I am ill
I *need* to exercise, even when I'm tired	I listen to my body and exercise accordingly
Eating well for my body takes too much effort	I love nourishing my body

These are just some examples of how you can reframe your limiting self-beliefs and start to change the way you think and feel. You can replace your old beliefs with new ones; you can choose to change your beliefs – *you* have control over how you think!

YOUR BELIEFS

Using the table below, list your current limiting self-beliefs and see how you could reframe them.

Existing Relationship Beliefs	New Relationship Beliefs
Existing Work Beliefs	New Work Beliefs
Existing Money Beliefs	New Money Beliefs
Existing Health Beliefs	New Health Beliefs

Your past does not have to define who you are today. The beliefs you have lived with until now do not have to influence who you are and how you interact in the world around you.

Your beliefs may be so ingrained in you that even identifying them can be a challenge in itself, so take your time and work on one at a time. Bizarre as it sounds, these beliefs have, over years, become your safety net. They are what keeps you from moving forward and even though they are not actually helping you, we sometimes feel safer with what we know rather than embarking on change. As the saying goes, 'Better the devil you know than the devil you don't'!

Once you have thought about your own limiting self-beliefs and put them down on paper, it's time to start challenging them in order to create new ones.

1. Taking each old belief, start by asking yourself:

➡   What outcome would I like? (If it's work-related it might be asking for a pay rise or not feeling guilty about leaving work on time.)

➡   What is stopping me getting the outcome I want?

➡   Is what is stopping me based on fact or truth?

2. Now start to really question your current belief:

➡   Is my belief real?

➡   Have I always thought this way?

➡   Why?

➡   Can I remember a time when I thought differently?

➡   If my best friend told me the same belief, how would I react?

➡   Is this belief getting me what I want?

➡   Is this a helpful belief?

➡   If I told my best friend about my belief, what would they say?

Having worked through the first two steps you may start to see cracks in your beliefs and begin to see that holding on to them does not serve you well. Now I want you to look at what it will look at if you keep holding on to your belief.

➡   What will happen if you *don't* change your belief?

➡   What will change if you *don't* change your belief?

➡   What will happen to you in your work, relationships, emotions, health?

➡   What are the benefits of not changing?

➡   Why is it important for you to change your belief?

Challenging your limiting self-beliefs can bring up emotions you have suppressed over years. Anger at parents or teachers for not encouraging you or believing in you. Anger at yourself for not believing in yourself. Use these emotions to motivate yourself to change your beliefs and create new positive self-beliefs. It can help to think of this new belief in the third person, as if you were looking at someone else and how they would behave and feel with this new belief.

Choose a new positive belief. This might be scary, and you might still think you don't deserve this new belief, but stick with it!

- How would it feel to have this new belief?
- What would you believe about yourself?
- How would others see you?
- How would your life change?
- What would be the benefits to you?
- What would change in the short term?
- What would change in the long term?

Changing beliefs and behaviours doesn't happen overnight; it takes time and commitment. It's easy to slip back into old patterns of negative thoughts, they've been with you for years and they are deeply ingrained in you. Be gentle and kind in the process of creating change. Focus on exactly what you want to change, take small steps, recognise when you're slipping back into old beliefs and challenge them.

I still have limiting self-beliefs that pop up every now and then. When that happens, I accept them and go through the steps I've listed above. I value my self-care and when I do that it allows me to gently change beliefs I've held on to for no good reason.

We all have limiting self-beliefs. Your best friend would probably laugh at you if you told them yours! Separate your self-beliefs into different categories and challenge them. Create new beliefs. Repeat!

PERFECTIONISM

You might think that someone who is a perfectionist would be quite good at managing themselves. After all, they are perfectionists, right? Wrong! Perfectionists create a distorted set of values and beliefs that puts them under pressure to strive to have unrealistically high standards. This behaviour often starts in school with exams and/or sports and continues into adulthood. These thoughts and behaviours are often driven by themselves and not by family or teachers, but more by a self-imposed ideal that being perfect means they will be thought well of. In essence they use achievements, rather than the person they are, to justify their value. Which in turn means that if they don't reach their self-imposed target, their internal critic has a field day and impacts hugely on their self-esteem and confidence, which has a knock-on effect on physical and mental wellbeing.

The characteristics of perfectionists can lead to burnout because of the high standards they set and the higher risk of not attaining those standards *all* the time. To others, perfectionists can seem very rigid in their outlook and way of managing things, both at home and at work. And to make matters worse for the perfectionist, they are always raising the self-imposed bar. Once the standards are achieved they impose even higher ones which can lead to higher stress levels, and so the road to burnout begins. It's really important to understand the difference between setting new goals and having healthy manageable standards to live by, knowing how to learn by mistakes rather than allowing your inner critic to beat you up and creating more self-imposed standards, which has a damaging effect on you.

A good measure of standard is effort rather than outcome. By that I mean that if your standard is doing the best you can with the resources you have (both physically and emotionally), then that's a good starting point. Perfectionism at its highest level is impossible, it is a waste of good healthy energy, it can be a waste of time and most of all, it can be massively damaging to your health. Strive to be the best *you* can be, not to be perfect!

1. What are your beliefs?

Beliefs	Why do you think this way?
I must ...	
I mustn't ...	
I should ...	
I shouldn't ...	
I can ...	
I can't ...	

2. What are your perfectionist behaviours?

Behaviour	Tick	Why do I do this? How does it make me feel?
Sets very high self-standards and expects no mistakes		
Expects high standards of others and is critical if they're not met		
Tendency to be self-critical and have low self-esteem		
Fears getting things wrong		
Takes mistakes personally; sees them as failure		
Becomes emotional when mistakes are made		
Inner critic always switched on		
Organised		
Likes lists		
High level of attention to detail		

Difficulty prioritising tasks		
Needs recognition for effort		
Sees criticism as a personal attack		
Repeatedly checks work/tasks		
Never fully happy with end product		
Will work outside working hours		
Doesn't like risk-taking for fear of failure		
Fears others' judgement		

3. What are the benefits to you of being a perfectionist?

4. What are the disadvantages for you of being a perfectionist?

Now, having looked at your answers above, which of your beliefs could you look at changing? Which behaviours do you think you could relax so that you could work at preventing burnout?

Knowing the damaging effects that being a perfectionist can have on you is one thing, but here is a list of areas that you can look at to start changing the negative effects being a perfectionist can cause before burnout happens.

- **80:20 rule.** This is one of my favourite tips and one I like to adapt to lots of different areas in life, for example exercise, nutrition, sleep, clutter, mindfulness and general wellness. Working at anything and expecting 100% perfection all the time is a huge pressure on you and not a realistic goal. Working at getting different aspects of your life 80% right is a much more realistic goal. The brain acknowledges positive achievements with a positive mindset, and likewise it sees not getting something perfect as failure.

- **Be kind to you.** I grew up in a world where I was told 'self-praise is no praise'. I spend my days telling myself and my clients that self-praise is great! When you get something done that has been a struggle, give yourself a pat on the back. Whether it's practising the 80:20 rule, leaving work on time or simply allowing yourself to relax, celebrate rather than think, 'I could have done that better'!

- **Check in with your expectations.** If you find yourself slipping and the negative self-talk getting louder in your head, take a minute to review the exercises you filled in above and see how you could realign your expectations of yourself to reduce the negative self-talk. Maybe see how the 80:20 rule could apply to whatever you're doing.

- **Ask for help.** Asking for help can be seen as a sign of weakness. I would like to tell you now that that is not true. In fact, asking for help is a sign of strength – it shows that you are willing to learn if you're unsure what you're doing, and you're willing to be part of a team (even if it's an at-home team). Recognising that asking for help is beneficial rather than a hindrance allows you to get the task done and connect with others. You might also learn a different way of doing something that may not be as stressful as doing it alone. Win–win.

- **Practise.** Having all these new ways of looking at things can be hard and actually changing behaviours can seem daunting. Take five

minutes to write down why you are changing your current beliefs
and behaviours that are causing you issues.

I often get clients who struggle with what they do well to do this exercise.
It's human habit to focus on what we don't do well rather than on what
we do well, which in turn makes us focus on the failures rather than the
achievements. With that in mind, I'd like to you think about these two
questions:

1. What do you do well?

2. What do you feel you don't do so well?

It's very common to write loads for the second question and leave the first
question blank! Think about home and work, think about things you do
without even thinking about it, think about family and friends. Write down
every small thing you do well, however insignificant you think it is.

What I do well	What I don't feel I do well

Why did I ask you to do this? Well, when you're struggling and about to
beat yourself up for not reaching the high bar you set for yourself, take this
out and look at all that you do well; see in black and white how competent
you are at so much!

Perfectionists create a distorted set of values and beliefs that puts them under
pressure to strive to reach unrealistically high standards. Perfectionism at its
highest level is impossible, it is a waste of good healthy energy, it can be a waste
of time, and most of all, it can be massively damaging to your health. Strive to be
the best **you** can, not to be perfect!

PERSONALITY TYPE

Have you ever taken the Myers–Briggs Type Indicator test (MBTI)? This is an assessment that aims to measure your personality preferences along four different dimensions. The Myers–Briggs personality test is based on the personality type indicator developed by Katharine Cook Briggs and her daughter Isabel Briggs Myers in the 1940s and it was based on Carl Jung's psychological research. The test is based on a series of questions that gather information on how you respond or relate to various situations.

The answers to these questions are then calculated to determine your individual personality type. The idea behind the test is that in order to have a more satisfied work life, people need to better understand themselves, which can then help them choose a job that best suits their personality.

It is used widely in the corporate world, but there are many independent and online tools you can use if you're curious to know what your personality type is and how it relates to your work. The MBTI helps people answer the following questions: Where do you focus your attention? Where do you get your energy? How do you prefer to take in information? How do you make decisions? How do you organise the world around you?

The Myers–Briggs test will not tell you which specific career you should choose, but you can use the results of the tests to look at the pros and cons of different working environments and see how they match with what you'd like to do. There are numerous test you can do online, but the official one is at www.mbtionline.com/TaketheMBTI.

Your personality plays an important role in the way you cope with negative situations. Your personality can be the reason you have poor coping skills, or it can hinder your ability to have good ones. That is why even personality is one of the causes of burnout.

Often it is people who are involved with working and caring for other people (either in work or at home) who are the first to suffer from burnout. These are the people whose personality type is focused on caring and who continue to give at the detriment of their own self-care. Their personality type is why they push themselves, causing burnout to creep up on them. In wanting to help everyone, they take on more work and tasks than they can handle.

The Myers–Briggs personality traits are broken down into four different areas: Energy, Information, Decisions and Organising. Each of these areas is then broken down into two different extremes of the scale, so your result will be based on the four areas with an extreme of each area. In simple terms, my Myers–Briggs personality trait is 'Introversion/Intuition/Feeling/Judging (IIFJ)'.

Extroversion vs. Introversion: where do you get your energy? A strong extrovert who is in an office or working alone all day by themselves will become restless and bored. Extroverts tend to need outside stimuli and interaction to help maintain their enthusiasm. They enjoy being out in the world and interacting with others, so if they work in a situation where that doesn't happen, their energy levels (and mood) will begin to slip.

Conversely, introverts can get easily overwhelmed by too much external stimuli. They prefer positions where they can work alone and have quiet, reflective time. A job in sales or customer service, or working in an open-plan office, could create feelings of stress for an introvert and they could be susceptible to burnout.

Sensing vs. Intuition: how do you take in information? Sensors personalities like facts and details, and are more suited to structured work environments, whereas intuitives are generally open to multiple variables and they tend to respond negatively to rigid work environments and/or repetitive processes. Intuitives are more comfortable working on the creative process of work whereas sensors are the ones who like to get projects completed!

Thinking vs. Feeling: how do you prefer decisions to be made?
Thinkers want to see a logical approach to decision-making and they crave
results that make clear sense based on facts – they don't bring emotion
into their reasoning. Feelers, on the other hand, are the opposite. They are
more likely to see the emotional and sociological sides of decisions first and
facts second. In both home and work situations, feelers tend to be better
at understanding the need to compromise, whereas this way of thinking
would frustrate a thinker.

Burnout can ensue if you are in a position where you have to make
decisions that are at odds with your personality preference.

Additionally, thinkers and feelers could both get frustrated if their boss's
decisions are made in ways they don't understand or relate to. The more we
understand what our personality type is, and those around us, the more we
are able to adjust our own behaviours and responses accordingly.

Judging vs. Perceiving: how do you organise your world? Judgers like
things to be ordered and routine, whereas perceivers like things to be
spontaneous and flexible. You can probably easily tell who is a judger and
who is a perceiver in work or even at home with family members. In a
meeting a judger would want a plan of action and to understand exactly
how the plan would be achieved, while a perceiver might view the same
meeting as a place to chat and brainstorm without any structure.

In a work environment, being disorganised can be a major stressor for
judgers, who like to know what exactly is expected of them. Perceivers
might feel too constrained by these limits and would prefer the freedom to
be creative. Perceivers often like jobs that are unpredictable like planning
for events or emergency services or even working at a new start-up where
they can invent the process.

INTROVERTED OR EXTROVERTED?

'There is no such thing as a pure introvert or extrovert. Such a person would be in the lunatic asylum.' **Carl G. Jung**

The descriptions *introvert* and *extrovert* do not just relate to our personality type, but also to *where we get our energy from*. Recognising which camp you largely fall into means that you can ensure that you recharge your energy levels accordingly. Interestingly, I had always thought I was an extrovert; in fact if you asked anyone who knows me they would laugh at the thought that I could be an introvert! When I was younger I attended drama classes and although I loved them, I found them utterly tortuous. I can still feel the onset of butterflies in my stomach when I think of it, but at home I was a show girl. I was happy to entertain those close to me and enjoyed putting on little shows. When I began drinking alcohol this new crutch gave me the false confidence to be able to engage socially and blend in. I didn't realise how energy-draining it was trying to be as sociable as my friends. For as long as I can remember my hangovers would be beyond body-wrecking, but I thought everyone else's were the same, so in good Irish fashion I said yes to going out even though I was physically and emotionally exhausted. I persevered because I had no idea I was an introvert. I probably didn't even know what the word meant. Being an introvert and trying to live as an extrovert was definitely a huge factor in my burnout and increased alcohol abuse.

In my twenties, when I worked in the music industry, an industry that is as socially interactive as it gets, I would interact with people every day, and my evenings were equally social, and to give myself the energy to engage with it all, I would drink. This is where my negative relationship with alcohol first began. To me introverted people were shy; they couldn't or didn't want to engage with others as they preferred to listen rather than partake in conversations. I am not that! I love to engage in conversations, I love people, I love to be asked to social events. However, I now know my limitations and when I need to leave the 'party'. For me it took giving up alcohol to realise I was never an extrovert. I am a very happy introvert, and knowing this has allowed me to work better professionally and personally. I know when I have to take a 'life-pause' in order to recharge my batteries and, most important, I know how vital it is for me to do that so that I can mind myself, function better and avoid burnout.

Introverts (or those with introverted tendencies) tend to recharge their batteries by spending time alone. They lose energy from being around people for long periods of time, particularly large crowds. I explain this to clients as like being able to plug yourself into a wall socket, in a room on your own, and recharge yourself.

Extroverts, on the other hand, get their energy from being around other people. Extroverts actually find their energy is drained when they spend too much time alone. They recharge their batteries by being social. It's not that they fear missing out on social activities, but that's where they feel fully charged.

Ambiverts: In the middle of the scale of introverts and extroverts there is an energy source called ambiverts or **introverted extroverts**. Many of us tend to lean towards introvert or extrovert, but there are some people who fall between the two, and these people are called ambiverts.

Ambivert people get their energy source from both being introverted and extroverted. While they enjoy being around people, after long periods of time this will start to drain them. Equally, they enjoy times of solitude and quiet, but may not do too well with extended periods of isolation. Ambiverts recharge their energy levels with a combination of social interaction and alone time.

There is lots of interesting science about introverts/extroverts and brain function, but I really just want you to be able to see how recognising where you get your energy source from can help you to manage your self-care in a healthier way. If you are more of an extrovert than an introvert, taking a job where you may be on your own a great deal might not be the best option for you. Equally, if you are more of an introvert, working in an environment where you are constantly being bombarded by people all day every day might not help you recharge your energy levels and could therefore lead to burnout. Noticing where you fall on the scale allows you to understand your own needs. If creating pockets of alone time is what you need to keep your emotional energy levels high, make them happen; and if being around people is your energy source, make sure social interaction with others is part of your self-care routine.

SOCIAL CONNECTIONS

The importance of social connections is often undervalued, especially for introverts. If you consider yourself a naturally social person, then you know that spending time with friends and family makes you happier (well, most of the time). But even if you're introverted and prefer spending time by yourself, it may be that you've fallen into a habit of spending too much time alone. Even introverts need to connect with others. Another way we can retreat from social interactions is from the effects of burnout caused in either in the workplace or at home.

Research into the impact of social connections on our health and lifespan has been going on for over 50 years, with numerous studies concluding that we humans are social beings who require connections with other humans in order to thrive. Social connections, such as friendships, relationships with family members and closeness within a community, are so closely related to wellbeing and personal happiness, the two can practically be equated.

In fact, a lack of social connection is a greater overall health risk than smoking! Being lonely impacts your immune system as well as your susceptibility to anxiety and depression.

Connection is contagious. Research conducted at Harvard looking into how social connection within friendship networks impacts us found that the positive influence is contagious in ways even those experiencing the effects often did not recognise. Love, kindness and happiness can all be spread through solid human connections. Deep connections, like healthy relationships, seem to be the most beneficial, but even more casual connections with people we don't really know can still create positive effects. It's good to talk!

Connection is about perception. When I was in the depth of burnout I can honestly say I felt lonely even when I was socialising with family or friends. I was so burnt-out that my perception of how I viewed those relationships was skewed by my own thoughts. I was so disconnected from my life that I couldn't see the wood for the trees. Your connectedness to others is less about what you do and more about how you view your relationships. Taking the time to feel grateful for the people in your life actually deepens those bonds, whether or not it changes any of the outward behaviour between you or not.

Connections can be cultivated. The good news is that even introverts can build connections with others! In today's technological world, it's easier than ever to 'find your tribe', whether in person or through social media or email. Technology makes it easier to be connected to friends all the time. The great news is that all positive connections have health and happiness benefits, so participating in any form of positive social interaction is building up your so-called connection bank, and the more you connect, the happier you'll feel and the more likely you'll be to build even more connections.

FEAR OF CHANGE

If you haven't already seen the video of Will Smith, actor and motivational speaker, talking about fear, I urge you to go to YouTube and search for 'Will Smith – Facing Your Fears'. Fear is one of the most debilitating emotions we can have. It can cause us to stay in relationships we know are not healthy, stop us having a voice and speaking up for ourselves, hinder personal and professional growth, heighten our anxiety and immobilise us, preventing us moving forward.

Generally speaking, we don't like change either, so coupling fear and change together is a recipe for stagnation. Fear of change can be a huge factor in staying in a place in your life where you feel undervalued. Fear is very closely linked to your limiting self-beliefs. What if you make a change in your life and it doesn't work out the way you wanted it to? What if you move jobs and you still feel bad? What if ...? The list goes on and on. Until you make the leap and trust yourself, you will never know if you can succeed. I regularly tell my clients (and my boys) that success and failure are merely perceptions of an outcome. Every day we experience subtle changes in life that we hardly notice; we accept them without question with the same familiarity as yesterday.

You can learn more from failure than success. If you really want to live a life that makes you happy, you have to be open to change and to welcome it with a sense of enthusiasm and excitement.

Dr Ian Robertson, Professor of Psychology at Trinity College, Dublin, and founding director of Trinity College Institute of Neuroscience, has applied his incredible research to the pressures of everyday life. In talking to him about the brain's ability to create the feeling of anxiety around fear, and fear of change, he explained a very simple exercise you can do to reframe how you view fear: 'Anxiety and excitement have a very similar set of bodily symptoms which reflect activation of the sympathetic autonomic nervous system, and saying to yourself, "I feel excited", when you are feeling anxious can help to turn a negative emotion of anxiety into a more positive one of excitement.'

AISHLING'S STORY

When Aishling came to see me a few years ago she was only 22 years old. She was very emotional, unhappy in her job, and although she loved her boyfriend she was unhappy in the relationship. She was exhausted and the slightest disagreement with her boyfriend turned into a full-blown row that she always regretted afterwards. Over the last few years she had dipped in and out of attending therapy sessions and would have short bursts of feeling okay, but it never lasted long as she didn't have the energy to keep up the appearance of being okay.

More recently Aishling came back to see me feeling the same way. She was due to go on what should have been a great trip to the States for a two-week holiday with her boyfriend, to visit a college friend who lived there. There were lots of activities and adventures planned and, on the surface, she knew she should be looking forward to it, but she wasn't. She was completely unmotivated about it; in fact she had a sense of dread about the whole trip. During the session she also said that while she liked her job, she felt undervalued and overworked. To sum it up, she couldn't find anything positive in her life other than her dog.

When Aishling was 11 years old she was diagnosed with type 1 diabetes. This came out of nowhere – overnight, she was thrown into the biggest change of her young life. Aishling is one of four girls and while all the other siblings were eating sweets at Christmas, sugar-laden cakes at birthdays and didn't have to have five injections every day, Aishling had to live her day-to-day life very differently. At 11 years old her resentment and anger to this sudden change in her once-normal life was huge. A few years later, her family decided to move to Brussels due to her father's work commitments, a move that now meant she would be leaving all her friends and starting school afresh, it was another change in her life that was sudden and she had no control over. Before finishing secondary school in Brussels, Aishling's family moved back to Dublin. By now she had made friends in Brussels and the thought of coming home and slotting back into her old school unnerved her and again left her feeling out of control. Trying to pick up where she left off with her schooling and her friends filled her with even more anxiety, but she did it – she had no choice. When she was in first year in college her parents and younger siblings moved abroad again, and Aishling stayed at home, worked part-time and completed her studies.

The most interesting observation I made was her emotional attachment to change, any change. Aishling had, over the last ten years, attached the emotion 'fear' to 'change'. It was so deep-rooted in her that she initially didn't see how her fear of change could be impacting on her present life. She found any change at all left her feeling completely out of control. And the energy it took to feel angry about the changes in her life, however small, left her burnt-out. Changes in work, with new responsibilities or temporary workloads, would result in feeling undervalued and overworked; changes in her weekly routine annoyed her; holidays became something to fear rather than enthuse over because she didn't know what to expect (more change).

In order to help Aishling start to see the pattern of her behaviour based on an emotion attached to past events, I got her to write the word 'change' in big letters on the middle of a page. From there she drew lines outwards and wrote down each big change that had had a negative impact on her life. The initial response was quite amazing. Once she could see in black and white how the different situations all led back to the word 'change' she began to understand how her fear of change in big life events had seeped into her fear of change in pretty much everything in her life. Understanding the causes has helped Aishling work through altering how she views change in her life. Using a selection of tools from her growing toolkit, she is slowly letting go of her fear. She is happier in work, her relationship is less fraught, and she is learning to see that change happens every day: sometimes we have control over it and sometimes we don't. Whichever way, it's how we respond to it that matters.

To get the ball rolling and challenge you to step out of your comfort zone, these are some steps you can use to overcome fear of change.

Understand that life is change and change happens every day. From the moment you are born, you experience change. Having spent nine months living comfortably in your mother's womb, you are catapulted into the world with no advance warning. Life then becomes a series of changes that we don't necessarily want – we may need them but we don't necessarily want them! Some changes can be perceived as emotionally painful, such as being separated from a parent, starting crèche or school. We attach an emotion to this change and that emotion is fear. Understandably, we seek to avoid it. It makes sense that our emotional attachment (fear) is one of the main reasons we dislike change so much. It is why we stay in jobs that make us unhappy, refuse to let go of relationships that cause us pain and stay stuck in behaviours and habits that don't work for us. Life is change and change happens every day. Don't view change as a punishment or something you're not in control of, but see it as an opportunity to grow, improve and to learn new things. Whatever is happening in your life is teaching you something, so ask yourself: What can I learn from this? What is happening for me?

Accept the situation for what it is and look at what you can change to make it work for you! Accepting your current situation is the first step to embracing change. This doesn't mean you have to resign yourself that this is it. What I mean by this is that we don't have to passively accept things and become a victim of our environment. Acceptance requires courage, determination, honesty and – my favourite phrase – 'personal responsibility'. When you start to become aware of those parts of yourself or your environment that you are uncomfortable with, the ones you don't want to face or admit to but that you would like to change, you are in a place to start seeing change as exciting and not something to fear.

Failure is a perception. When I ask clients why they are afraid of change, the most common answer is the fear of failure. Our minds think that the only way to avoid failure is to stay static and do nothing. We prefer not to take any action and live life as a movie extra rather than as the lead star. Let me tell you, making mistakes is part of the learning curve. I should know – I've made enough of them! When you make mistakes, learn from them, note what didn't work (not what 'failed') and use these learnings to improve yourself. When babies learn to walk, they fall time and time again. That is not failure! Babies don't suddenly give up and think, 'Oh well, that didn't work so I'll just sit here for the rest of my life.' Whether they were laughed at or with, they get back up and keep on working at it until they get it. What would it be like to channel that thought and keep that same steely determination when faced with times when we 'fall' in life? It is our limiting self-belief, judgement from others and fear of change that paralyses us and stops us moving forward. Recognising the emotional attachment we associate with fear allows you to cut ties and view change from a fact-based viewpoint rather than one based on an emotion. Whenever I have a little wobble with fear of failure I think of Richard Branson, a man who used his dyslexia as a strength, not a failing.

Celebrate! I always find it amazing how we focus on what doesn't work rather than what we have done well. When I used to collect the boys from school, rather than asking them, 'How was your day?' I changed the script to, 'Tell me one good thing that happened today.' A simple change in how you view something can have an incredibly powerful impact on how you view your achievements. By changing the question, the boys would tell me about the goal they scored at lunchtime, the fact that they ate *all* their lunch, about the new thing they did in school … They focused on small positive achievements rather than perceived failures. By celebrating the little things every day, we retrain our minds to accept change as a positive experience. The small victories motivate us to believe in ourselves. I've written an entire section (in Week 11) on gratitude and the benefits it has on how you feel. Use your gratitude journal to write down at least one thing every day that you see as a personal achievement. It doesn't matter how small or big you think it is, and it can be work-related or something you did at home. Write it down and celebrate what you've done, not what you haven't!

Personal responsibility. It is all too easy to fall into the pattern of thinking we don't have control over our lives. And on a certain level we cannot change what happens in life or how others behave around us, but we can take personal responsibility for ourselves and change our behaviour in response to our environment and those around us. We can learn to respond rather than react. To have personal responsibility means learning to own your 'stuff' and take back your ability to respond to events. To know the difference between trying to get others to change their behaviour and focusing on changing your own behaviours.

Be kind and patient. Rome wasn't built in a day! Getting to a place of embracing change takes time; it doesn't happen overnight. Think about how you react to someone when you are looking for them to action something quickly. Do you get impatient or are you patient? Impatience is a reaction. Patience is a response. Patience is a muscle that needs to be exercised every day, which is why I am a big fan of mindfulness and belly breathing. If you react impatiently to others, the chances are you react in the same way to yourself. Be kind and patient to yourself at all times.

Step outside your comfort zone. Do one thing this week that takes you outside your comfort zone. It could be talking to a colleague at work, cooking something new or trying a new gym class. Do one small thing that you know you will follow through with. See how you feel after you've done it. And next week do something else. Write a list of small things that you'd like to do and each week do one. Notice that the sky doesn't fall in on you and life still goes on, and then celebrate making those changes and not being fearful of them!

> 'Fear is not real. The only place that fear can exist is in our thoughts of the future. It is a product of our imagination, causing us to fear things that do not at present and may not ever exist. That is near insanity. Do not misunderstand me, danger is very real, but fear is a choice.' **Will Smith**

Week 5

Practical steps: addressing the basics

Last week you got to know your personality type in a new light. This week you can start to address what I call the 'four basics' – sleep, nutrition, exercise and clutter – that may be causing you to feel out of control and slightly chaotic. As I said earlier, you may find that you're doing well in certain areas in this book, and if you do, great! But remember, this book is about layers, stripping back the unhealthy behaviours that don't work for you and replacing them with healthy behaviours that support you. Imagine trying to run a marathon without having trained. You might complete it, but at a cost to your physical and mental wellbeing. Well, the same can be said for day-to-day living. If you don't have the basics right, you're setting yourself up for a hard slog. Once you've addressed your four basics in Week 5 and you've spent some time working through Week 4, it's time to start learning and putting into practice some new tools to add to your 'layers'.

SLEEP

'Lose an hour in the morning, and you will spend all day looking for it.'
Richard Whately

'Ten years ago, I collapsed from burnout and exhaustion, and it's the best thing that could have happened to me.' These are the words of the amazing Ariana Huffington, who, among many other career achievements, has written an entire book about sleep, *The Sleep Revolution*. This is a quote from her book, and for me it sums up the utter importance of sleep. 'Just as we wouldn't eat off dirty dishes, why would we settle for going through the day with anything less than the full power and potential of our brains?' asks Huffington.

Why is sleep important? This seems like a very obvious question, but remember, sleep deprivation is a form of torture. Interestingly a few years ago a report by the US Senate Select Committee on the CIA's detention and interrogation programme following the 9/11 terrorist attacks stated that among the 'enhanced interrogation techniques' used was sleep deprivation. Research has shown that prolonged sleep deprivation is an especially dangerous form of torture because it attacks both your mental and physical health. You will often hear new parents complain of 'baby brain' – their minds are working at a slower rate due to lack of sleep.

The damage from sleep deficiency can creep up on you gradually over time; equally it can slow your reactions, making you less likely to react quickly in high-risk situations – an extreme example is someone falling asleep while driving. Sleep deprivation can affect how well you think, react, work, learn and get along with others. The way you feel when you're awake really depends on what happens while you're sleeping. During sleep, your body is working to repair itself after working hard all day. In children and teens, sleep also helps support growth and development.

HEALTHY BRAIN FUNCTION AND EMOTIONAL WELLBEING

Simply put, sleep helps your brain work properly. While you're sleeping, your brain is preparing for the next day. Cells are being repaired that allow you to keep learning and storing information. On a medical note, research at the University of Rochester Medical Centre in the States shows that brain cells shrink while we sleep, allowing fluid to literally wash the brain clean and get rid of the toxic build-up that occurs in the brain from working hard all day. Imagine your brain is like your teeth – just as your teeth need to be brushed to get rid of plaque, your brain needs to be cleaned too. During the day, when your brain is working hard having conversations, processing information or making decisions, it is forming its own form of plaque, which needs to be cleaned away each night in order to function at its optimum level the next day. When you sleep, that is exactly what is happening.

Sleep also plays an important role in your physical health. For example, sleep is involved in healing and repairing your body. When you're ill, the non-medical advice is to rest and get some sleep to allow the body to repair itself and heal.

Sleep deficiency also increases the chance of obesity in all age groups. Getting consistent good sleep helps maintain the hormones that make you feel hungry (ghrelin) or full (leptin). When you don't get enough sleep, your level of ghrelin goes up and your level of leptin goes down. This is partly why when you're sleep-deprived you feel hungrier than when you're sleeping regularly. Sleep also supports healthy growth and development. Hormones that boost muscle mass and repair cells and tissues are released when you sleep. Even your immune system depends on sleep to stay healthy. Ongoing sleep deficiency can change the way your immune system responds to minor ailments like colds and flus, making you more prone to recurring illnesses.

DAYTIME PERFORMANCE

Studies also show that sleep deprivation can affect the way the brain works during the day. If you're sleep-deprived, you may struggle with making decisions, solving problems, controlling your emotions and behaviour, and, interestingly, you may find it difficult to cope with change. Sleep deprivation has also been linked to a higher risk of depression, suicide and risk-taking behaviour. It may also cause problems with how you interact with others, both at home and work.

Getting enough quality sleep helps you function well throughout the day. People who are sleep-deficient are less productive at work and school. They take longer to finish tasks, have a slower reaction time – so are at higher risk of having or causing an injury – and can make mindless mistakes. Studies show that sleep deficiency impairs your driving ability as much as, or more than, being drunk.

After several nights of losing sleep – even a loss of just one to two hours per night – your ability to function suffers as much as if you hadn't slept at all for a night or two.

It's become increasingly common to hear, 'Oh, I only had five hours' sleep last night', or, 'I don't need a lot of sleep.' Even with limited or poor-quality sleep, you may still think that you can function well. A lot of people aren't aware of the risks of being sleep-deprived. More often, they do not even realise that they're sleep-deficient.

RESETTING YOUR SLEEP PATTERN

Motty Varghese, a senior respiratory and sleep physiologist at St James's Hospital who also has a private practice specialising in cognitive behavioural therapy for insomnia (CBTi), stresses the following points in helping us to understand that 'sleep is a priority and not a luxury'.

Establish a consistent bedtime and rising time, with a target of getting at least seven hours of sleep – since ideal sleep duration is seven to nine hours. Consistency is important because having the same wake period between our nightly episodes will help us to build adequate sleep drive. Sleep drive is our 'hunger for sleep'.

Our sleep and wakefulness is regulated by the presence or absence of natural light. When it is dark, our body recognises it as time for sleep and hence produces the sleepiness hormone melatonin, which induces sleep and we fall asleep and stay asleep. The much-talked-about blue light phenomenon tricks our body into thinking it is still daytime and delays our sleep onset. So make sure you turn off your blue light-emitting electronic devices two hours before your bedtime and also dim the lights at home.

There is very little doubt that burnout is often associated with anxiety and stress related to the situation that is causing burnout in the first place. Journalling is an effective way of keeping your anxiety at bay. If you are one of those anxious people, sit in a quiet corner in the early evening with a book and pen to write down your anxious thoughts. Examine the rationale of your thoughts and also look at your strengths and ability to deal with them. This will help to prevent you going to bed with those worries in your mind, which might affect your sleep.

The external/bedroom environment can also affect your sleep adversely as much your mind can. A cool, dark, quiet bedroom is essential to obtain a good night's sleep.

Drinking caffeine within eight hours of bedtime and alcohol within three hours of bedtime can also affect your sleep adversely.

> Sleep is an unsung hero of self-care. We need approximately seven hours' sleep a night, every night. Your brain and body need sleep in order to replenish all the hard work they did during the day. Sleep deprivation affects your brain's ability to function.

NUTRITION

> 'Let food be thy medicine, and medicine be thy food.' **Hippocrates**

If you have skipped to this section thinking there will be some new words of wisdom on how to shed a few pounds, you're going to be sorely disappointed. I have included this section not because I claim to be an expert on nutrition and diet, but to explain in plain English how crucial healthy nutrition is for you in relation to burnout. This is not about weight loss or gain; neither is it a pep talk on fad diets. It is simply a few home truths about why fuelling your body is hugely important in arming you with the body and mind you need to help navigate burnout. Your nutrition is as important to your body as sleep and exercise, and it is an area that can at times be pushed down to the bottom of your self-care pile. In 1826 a Frenchman named Jean Anthelme Brillat-Savarin wrote, 'Tell me what you eat, and I will tell you what you are.' If processed foods are your main food source and you overload on sugar from sunrise to sunset, not only will your body be on a go-slow, but your brain will too! Processed foods have an effect on your energy and how you think, so it should come as no surprise that continual consumption of a diet high in fat, sugar, salt, E numbers and lots of added ingredients you can't pronounce can contribute to burnout. Eating healthier, unprocessed foods will give you more energy, combat burnout, complement your sleep and exercise habits, and help your overall health.

SUGAR RUSH

In Week 3 I mentioned that we release the hormone cortisol as part of our fight-or-flight response. During this response we also release glucose (aka sugar) into our bloodstream in order to give our muscles a helping hand to respond quickly to our perceived stressor. Once our perceived stressor or stressful event is over our cortisol levels should return to normal, as should our glucose levels. When you are stressed, your body is producing glucose constantly because it thinks it needs to match the levels of cortisol your body is making, even when there are no actual stressors. In essence, your body is in a vicious cycle of being continually stressed, producing cortisol in response to 'fight-or-flight' and glucose to get your muscles ready for quick action. However, when you reach burnout, your body has been in such a state of constant stress that it ends up not generating enough cortisol (adrenal fatigue) and therefore not enough glucose to match it, so you can end up feeling light-headed and dizzy because your sugar levels are low. As a result, you go from too much glucose in your bloodstream to too little. Eating regular, healthy meals helps ensure that your blood sugar levels are kept consistent throughout the day. This in turn helps your adrenal glands and your brain function.

Here's a confession. I am a sugar addict. I am the person who buys the three-for-the-price-of-two Easter eggs and Christmas selection boxes, only to eat the first on the way home from the shops and then the remaining two because I don't want to be seen as the person who ate *all* the chocolate. I then have to go back to the shops and buy more. My sugar addiction has been with me for as long as I can remember and intensified when I quit drinking alcohol. At the time of writing, I have not touched alcohol in nearly 11 years, I consider myself a fairly healthy eater and I'm very conscious of the impact of 'good mood foods' on my body. However, I am real, and I am honest, and when I am feeling a bit under pressure with deadlines or children or I'm generally letting my own self-care slip, I crave sugar. I crave 'comfort' food. Toast with butter, milk chocolate (even the nasty ones that no one else likes), sugar-laden biscuits that give me a quick fix and spike my glucose levels.

What I have learned over time is that doing the same thing over and over and expecting a different response is not going to work, so for the sake of my health and sanity I took advice from an incredible lady called Catherine Joyce McIvor. Catherine explained that to ensure my sugar levels stayed, well, level, I had to eat regularly. You see, I was like most people I know and would skip breakfast because I wasn't hungry or was too busy. I would eat a small amount at lunch or skip that too. I'd start to eat around four o'clock, but by then my sugar levels had dropped and all I wanted was comfort food. By nine my need for sugar would be overwhelming and I would either eat the kids' stuff or make a quick trip to the shops. Roll on to having my nutrition revamped by Catherine and I now eat five meals a day. Yes, I have to be organised and, yes, sometimes it can be a pain in the ass, but the payoff is not craving sugar. No more headaches; my reasoning improved; I'd more energy for training; and, most noticeably, I stopped waking up in a sugar coma the following day. I do eat chocolate, but it's not that easy to consume massive amounts of 85% dark chocolate.

Changing the way I eat has impacted on my mood and my energy levels. Both are more even, I don't get mid-afternoon slumps or feel the need to eat large amounts of processed, sugary, salty food that negatively impacts my body. And yes, if there's birthday cake I eat a massive slice!

> Eat regularly throughout the day. Eat your breakfast. Look at the word, it says break-fast. After a night sleeping your body needs fuel to kick-start itself. Aim to eat every three to four hours. Any longer than that and you're asking for your sugar levels to drop. Make sure you drink water, all day, every day.

EXERCISE

We all know that exercise is good for you. But do you realise *how* good it is? I regularly tell my clients that 30 minutes of exercise every day can relieve stress and release hormones such as serotonin, dopamine and norepinephrine (happy hormones), which all work together to make you feel happier and more relaxed, can make you more productive, boost your energy levels and help you eat and sleep better. Not bad results for something as simple as a good walk every day.

> As with all new exercise regimes, please check with your doctor that you are physically healthy, and do not embark on any high-intensity exercise or drastic lifestyle changes without the guidance of a professional.

Looking at the research bit behind exercise, there are so many recent studies to show how exercise is not only good for your body but benefits your brain too. Research from the Institute for Brain Aging and Dementia shows that exercise can increase your brain's growth, which increases your learning skills and mental performance. One of the main reasons for this links back to not only all the good hormones being released but also the production of growth hormones, which maintain healthy connections in your cells, and these help you to focus better, learn new information more easily and switch between tasks more quickly.

There are many benefits of exercise to help reduce the symptoms of burnout or simply to ensure that you are keeping your self-care in check. However, it is also hugely important not to over-exercise. I know this may seem like a contradiction, but over-exercising when you are genuinely tired only puts more pressure and stress on your body and mind. Getting into a pattern of feeling guilty for not exercising when you feel you 'should' is completely counterproductive. Listen to your body. If you've had a hectic week and you've scheduled a high-intensity gym class into your day, maybe take a walk instead. Take personal responsibility for yourself and don't feel guilty about changing your plans!

Exercise supports you both physically and psychologically. Not only does it help to reduce stress and increase your ability to learn, it actually gives you more energy. A lot of people think that exercising will make them more tired and they find excuse after excuse to not do anything, but the truth is that when you exercise, more oxygen and nutrients are being transported around your body and brain, which gives you more energy, and that in turn helps you to think more quickly, focus and get stuff done.

An area that is often overlooked when talking about exercise is confidence. This isn't about getting all toned and changing your physique but about feeling strong and healthy. Feeling good about what your body can do, whether it's a 10k race or a 30-minute walk, has a positive impact on your confidence. This is not about comparing yourself to what someone else's body can do, it's about your self-care and sense of self-worth.

Exercise (and good nutrition) also go a long way to helping get a good night's sleep, and you know how I feel about sleep! Along with sleep, exercise also helps boost your immune system. But remember that exercise needs to be judged according to how you feel. If you are feeling run down, lower the intensity of your workouts; if your exercise is walking, reduce the time you walk until you start to feel better again. Exercise is there to lift you up, not drag you down.

FITTING IT IN

Take regular (this bit is important) physical activity. I recommend 30 minutes of activity every day.

If you are looking to kick the ass out of stress and you are already physically fit, kickboxing or boxing classes are a good way to fool the body into thinking it is in real 'fight' mode, while letting out aggression in a controlled environment also reduces your cortisol levels.

Aerobic activities such as running, walking, swimming or cycling can also reduce your cortisol levels. These activities recreate the 'flight' mode and reduce cortisol. These exercises also release endorphins, aka happy hormones, so it's win–win all round.

Your physical activity does not have to be intense. A gentle yoga class will not only help reduce your cortisol levels, it will also teach you mindfulness and positive breathing.

If you don't have enough time for a scheduled class a few times a week or can't commit to 30 minutes all at once each day, break up your activity into shorter daily bursts. Take three 10-minute walks daily or, and this is one everyone's heard, park further away from the office or get off the bus a few stops earlier, always allowing enough time to get to your destination so that you don't add more pressure to your day!

> Exercise has been proven to help reduce stress, increase energy levels, release lots of feel-good hormones, allow for better sleep, boost the immune system and improve overall health. All of this works at managing burnout rather than allowing burnout to manage you.

Clutter

> 'Clutter is not just physical stuff. It's old ideas, toxic relationships and bad habits. Clutter is anything that does not support your better self.' **Eleanor Brown**

It's easy to think that clutter means you're too busy with 'important' stuff to tidy and keep your space organised. I'm not just talking about the obvious clutter around you, I'm talking about the internal clutter of too many thoughts or, as I call it, 'busy thinking'. This kind of clutter can be paralysing and can create a feeling of being utterly overwhelmed.

There is also external clutter, the type of clutter you see around you – your desk, your home, your car, your phone, your computer, even your wardrobe! We continually purchase items that we think will make us feel better, but which actually add to our stress. Purchasing has become so immediate with online shopping that we can have almost instant gratification by buying items we don't actually need or even really want.

PHYSICAL CLUTTER

When was the last time you really decluttered your personal space? Whether you rent a room in a shared house, live at home with your parents or live in your own home, you have probably accumulated years' worth of things you don't actually need. We hold on to them for fear of letting go. We attach emotions to items, forgetting that *we* own the emotion; the items don't. Marie Kondo, who wrote *The Magical Art of Tidying Up*, takes clutter-clearing to a whole new level. Her method involves going through every item in your home and asking yourself if it 'sparks joy'. If it doesn't, bin it. I'm certainly not telling you to get rid of every single thing that does not 'spark joy' in your home; I'm talking about the clothes you don't wear, the books you've finished and will never re-read, the pots and pans that you never use, the drawer in your office desk you're too scared to open in case it won't close again. Clearing out the basic stuff you really and truly don't need. On its own, sitting down to a clean desk or getting into bed in a clutter-free bedroom won't change your entire outlook on life, but it will go a huge way, along with creating other positive habits, towards creating a calmer place for you to live.

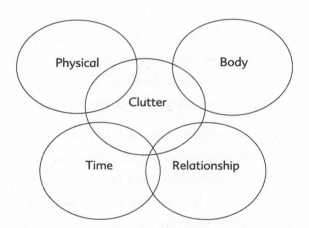

BODY CLUTTER

Are you looking to lose that elusive ten pounds that annoys you? Are you prone to skipping meals in favour of getting a job done? Do you start off the week with great plans to exercise and then don't? Or do you over-exercise when your body is tired? It always amazes me when I see how we can think our bodies are invincible and expect them to work like a high-performance car. We wouldn't drive it on empty and then wonder why the car ground to a halt!

TIME CLUTTER

Do you find that you never have enough time in the day to do everything you set out to do? Does lack of time stop you doing things for yourself? Do you find you're spending too much time checking social media yet by the end of the day you've no time left to eat healthily or mind yourself? In our ever-increasingly busy worlds, we have learned to fill our days up with so many things that we don't necessarily need to do. We sometimes get sucked into giving away our time to others out of a sense of duty or habit or a fear of saying no!

Learning to recognise the negotiable and non-negotiable things in your life will allow you to reclaim time for you. Non-negotiables are the things you will not negotiate on. They follow your values and beliefs and define what you will and won't accept from others, and also what you will and won't accept from yourself. On page 101 there is an exercise to help you understand and identify your own non-negotiables.

RELATIONSHIP CLUTTER

This is probably one of the trickiest forms of clutter to work on and also not as obvious as it seems. This is not just about your relationships with others but also your relationship with yourself. There is a lovely saying I heard years ago – 'People come into our lives for a reason, season or a lifetime' (Michelle Ventor). Sometimes we hold on to relationships that cause us pain and hurt but we keep them out of sense of duty. Take time to look at your relationships and make sure that they are healthy and mutually supportive. Toxic relationships with friends, work colleagues and family can cause stress and burnout – remember 'reason, season or lifetime'. And while you're doing a relationship audit, take a few minutes to see how your relationship is with yourself. Is your own internal dialogue toxic and causing you damage? There is a great book by psychologist Allison Keating called *The Secret Life of Adults*, which I highly recommend to anyone looking to explore this area of their lives a little further.

If all this seems a little overwhelming and even the thought of having to sort through drawers, rooms, relationships, and yourself, fills you with dread, start with one area. Start with something you know you will be able to manage. Personally, I find the Marie Kondo method a bit too drastic, but I do like the idea of tackling non-emotional areas first. So with that in mind, start with your office drawer, kitchen or a few drawers in your bedroom.

Mantras to remind yourself when clearing clutter in all areas of your life:

Less is more.

You will have what you need when you need it.

You can't take it with you.

Amassing material things is not the object of this game of life.

Toxic relationships are not healthy regardless of who they are with.

Week 6

Time management and goal setting

Week 6 is about creating new structures that align with who you *are* and not who you think you *should be*. You can't be all things to all people, so stop trying to be! There are a few exercises this week that will help you to clearly define what is important to you and how you can begin to focus on them. This week looks at figuring out what your non-negotiables are in life, why time management and routine are essential. I explain why multi-tasking is not your friend and how to manage yourself when you're being asked to do ten things at once! By using what you have learned about yourself in Week 4, you can now start to delve even deeper to create the changes that best suit you. Keep in mind that we are all different, you may already have some of these tools in place and therefore your focus might be more around understanding your personality type and how that is causing you to burn out.

So what else can you do to reduce the risk of burnout? Knowing the signs and symptoms is the starting point, and working on ensuring that your four cornerstones of sleep, nutrition, exercise and clutter are being given the attention they need is a good foundation, but what else can you do to reduce the risk of the negative effects of burnout?

The foundations, which are at the core of minding yourself and ensuring you have the energy to deal with the hectic life we exist in, are hugely important. If you're not paying attention to these, any other work you do for yourself is going to be much harder. Trust me, I've seen clients resist elements of them and struggle to see why they are not making any progress in changing behaviours that contribute to burnout. I'm going to provide you with practical tools you can use, the extra components you can begin to adopt to help live a better life for you.

NON-NEGOTIABLES VS. NEGOTIABLES

Setting your non-negotiables is important not only to free up time but also to ensure that you are meeting your priority needs.

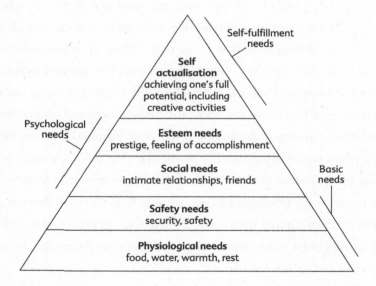

In order to identify your non-negotiables, it is a good idea to start by understanding what our basic needs, not our wants, are. Back in the 1950s, a psychologist by the name of Abraham Maslow developed a theory called the Hierarchy of Needs. Maslow was one of the founders of humanistic psychology, which focuses on a person's potential and the importance of their emotional growth and self-actualisation. Maslow's theory grew out of his interest in developing an area of psychology that was not based on clinical studies but rather focused on normal human growth and development.

Based on looking at our human growth and development, Maslow developed a pyramid system that classified all our basic needs into five different groups, and which he rated in terms of their importance for human development and survival. This was called Maslow's Hierarchy of Needs. The needs at the top of the pyramid were most important for the development of personality; however, and this is the important bit, he believed that the higher needs could not be fulfilled until the lower needs, or basic needs, such as physiological and safety needs, were met. In basic terms Maslow believed that we had to meet, and retain, each of the five stages in order, and if one of them wasn't being cared for, it would affect all the others. In essence, the stages are like building blocks. If one of the lower stages (your foundation needs) is not being met, it puts strain on the rest of the blocks, which can put your personal infrastructure under enormous strain. For example, if your safety needs are not being met, it will be difficult to focus on your self-esteem needs because your safety needs create a stable foundation. Our needs, according to Maslow, are:

1. Physiological needs. These are fairly obvious. They are the things that are vital to our survival: food, water, breathing, shelter. Maslow also included sexual reproduction in this level of the Hierarchy of Needs since it is essential for survival and procreation.

2. Security and safety needs. This is the second level of Maslow's hierarchy. People want control and order in their lives, so this need for safety and security contributes to our behaviours. Some of the basic security and safety needs are: financial security, health and wellness, safety against accidents and injury. Finding a job, trying to save money, and living in a safe neighbourhood are all examples of actions motivated by security and safety needs. Together, the safety and physiological levels of the hierarchy make up what is often referred to as the basic needs, or the foundations.

3. Social needs. These include such things as love, acceptance and belonging. At this, the third level, the need for emotional relationships is what drives human behaviour. Some of the things that satisfy this need include: friendships, romantic attachments, family, social groups, community groups, churches and religious beliefs. In order to avoid problems such as loneliness, depression and anxiety, it is important for people to feel loved and accepted by other people. Personal relationships with friends, family, and partners play an important role, as does involvement in other groups, for example sports clubs, book clubs and other group activities.

4. Esteem needs. The fourth level in Maslow's hierarchy is the need for appreciation and respect. When the needs at the bottom three levels have been met, the esteem needs begin to play a more prominent role in our motivating behaviour. According to Maslow, at this point it becomes increasingly important to gain the respect and appreciation of others. People have a need to accomplish things and then have their efforts recognised. Not being appreciated and/or recognised for one's efforts either at home or work is one of the main contributors to burnout. In addition to the need for feelings of accomplishment and prestige, the esteem needs include such things as self-esteem and personal self-worth. People need to feel that they are valued and to value themselves. People who are able to satisfy the esteem needs by achieving good self-esteem and the recognition of others tend to feel confident in their abilities. Hence self-esteem is the foundation for self-confidence. Those who lack self-esteem and the respect of others can develop feelings of inferiority. Together, the esteem and social levels make up what is known as the psychological needs of the hierarchy.

5. Self-actualisation needs. These are at the very top of Maslow's Hierarchy of Needs. 'What a man can be, he must be', Maslow explained, referring to the need people have to achieve their full potential as human beings. According to Maslow's definition of self-actualisation, 'It may be loosely described as the full use and exploitation of talents, capabilities, potentialities, etc. Such people seem to be fulfilling themselves and to be doing the best that they are capable of doing ... They are people who have developed or are developing to the full stature of which they are capable.'

Using the table below, write down what your non-negotiables are. They could be your kids, your family, your dog, your yoga class, whatever you value most. Then look at your negotiables. Is the evening class you randomly signed up for making you happy? Are you only attending each week for fear of being judged for leaving? If so, leave. It's negotiable. It is something you are doing that is eating into precious time that could reclaim. Are you spending more time on social media than you'd like? Check to see exactly how much time you're using. Scrolling on your phone may be eating up hours of your day, so view it as negotiable (unless, of course, it is part of your job) and release some time. To make it even easier, I suggest breaking your non-negotiables down into three areas – lifestyle (which is really your self-care), personal and professional – and see what is negotiable in order to de-clutter your time.

Lifestyle	
Non-Negotiables	*Negotiables*

Personal	
Non-Negotiables	*Negotiables*

Professional	
Non-Negotiables	*Negotiables*

MULTI-TASKING: WHY IT SERIOUSLY DOES NOT WORK

Imagine your brain is like a computer and you have a number of tabs open at the same time. The computer works, but maybe it's a bit slow. It takes a bit longer to switch from tab to tab. Well, that's your brain. The more tasks you have on the go at any given time, the slower you are to switch between them. Now imagine you shut down some of the tabs that are open on your computer – suddenly switching from tab to tab is faster.

Multi-tasking may seem like the only option you have to get through the enormous workload you face every day. But the hard reality is that multi-tasking doesn't work. In fact, it reduces your ability to complete each task efficiently and productively and that can result in added stress in your day, each and every day. If you're thinking, 'But I multi-task all the time, therefore I can multi-task', let me explain the science behind it.

The term multi-tasking was originally used to describe the workings and wiring of a computer, not human beings. In reference to computers, the term was used to describe how they could alternate between multiple tasks, i.e. switch back and forth between tasks. Over time the term was taken out of context and became a way of describing people's ability to work simultaneously on numerous tasks.

Even computers can't work on numerous commands or tasks simultaneously. They can, however, switch between tasks at lightning speed without having to think, get emotionally involved or feel resentful at doing too much work. But ask a computer to do too much, like having too many tabs open, and it will perform more slowly and may even freeze and shut down!

There is a big difference between being able to 'do' two or more things at once – obviously you can walk and talk, or eat and read at the same time – and being able to **focus** on two things at once. We can't think two different things at the same time. (This is also why mindfulness is so good at helping to relax and calm our body and brain.)

Researchers at Stanford University have found that multi-tasking is less productive than doing a single thing at a time. The researchers also found that people who are regularly bombarded with different forms of electronic information cannot pay attention, recall information, or switch from one job to another as well as those who complete one task at a time. Research has also shown that people who work in offices are interrupted approximately every 11 minutes of their working day and they then spend almost a third of the day recovering from these distractions. And with this level of distraction, we still put pressure on ourselves to complete our tasks, meet deadlines and think that multi-tasking will get us through our day.

'But I'm really good at multi-tasking!'

People often brag about their ability to multi-task; it's something they genuinely believe they are really good at and maybe even think they have a special skill for. The lovely researchers at Stanford University examined this possibility. In their research they tested groups of people based on their ability to multi-task and their belief that they did it well and that it boosted their work performance. The results showed that those people who multi-task a lot, and feel that it boosts their performance, were actually *worse* at multi-tasking than the people who preferred to do a single task at a time. The multi-taskers actually performed worse in their work because they had more trouble organising their thoughts, and they were *slower* at switching from one task to another. (Brains are not computers.)

> Multi-tasking reduces your productivity because your brain can only focus on one thing at a time. When you try to do two things at once, your brain lacks the ability to perform both tasks successfully. So shut down your mental computer tabs!

I want to highlight one area that I think is really important. There is research on just about everything we do in regard to our behaviour and what happens to our body, brain and emotions. One of the many interesting facts about the research into multi-tasking comes from researchers at the University of Sussex in the UK. They compared the amount of time people spend on multiple devices (such as texting while watching TV) to MRI scans of their brains. They found that high multi-taskers had less brain density in the anterior cingulate cortex (in the front part of the brain), a region responsible for empathy as well as cognitive and emotional control. The research showed that continually putting pressure on this part of the brain through trying to multi-task may result in a reduction in our empathy levels, our cognitive (rational) thinking and our ability to control our emotions. Neuroscientist Kep Kee Loh, the study's lead author, explained the implications of this: 'I feel that it is important to create an awareness that the way we are interacting with the devices might be changing the way we think and these changes might be occurring at the level of brain structure.' Knowing this should be enough to make you think twice about digital multi-tasking!

If you're prone to multi-tasking, or believe that you are unique and have a special skill in the art of multi-tasking, you may want to rethink and change this habit.

Multi-tasking in meetings and other social settings (texting, sending emails and trying to be present in where you are and who you are with) also indicates low self-awareness and social awareness, and these two emotional intelligence skills are vital to how we interact with others in work and at home.

So every time you multi-task you aren't just harming your performance in the moment; you may be damaging an area of your brain that's critical to your future and reducing two vital emotional intelligence skills.

Taking things task by task is more productive.

FIND BALANCE WITH YOUR WHEEL OF LIFE

Life is full of imbalances and will continue to throw curve balls your way. Nearly all of us are aware of work–life imbalance that throws so many areas in our lives off kilter, when we are so busy making a living that we are not actually living. We can be so focused on one project at work that we neglect our self-care, or our home life becomes our main focus and we forget to nurture our social lives.

Part of the problem is that we don't make the time to look at what areas of our lives are important to us, what is important to us and what aspects of our lives make us happy. Using a Wheel of Life will help you break down your life into small manageable segments and work through identifying the areas that are important and often neglected.

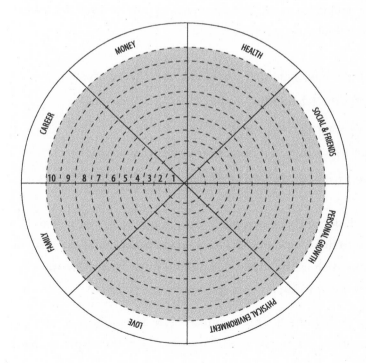

The Wheel of Life will enable you to take a step back and think about the different areas in your life. You'll be able to see what areas of your life you are happy with and those that need a boost. You'll discover where your imbalances lie, and although you might not be able to change everything, you'll be able to focus on what you can change and let go of feelings of helplessness over the areas you can't. Using the Wheel of Life helps you to assess what you'd like your life to look like and how you can achieve this. This well-used tool will help you to see where your current priorities are, and if they need refocusing.

Start by taking a look at each area in your wheel and rate it from 1 to 10 on how satisfied you are in each, 1 being the least satisfied and 10 being the most. Fill this in for each segment. Take some time with this and be really honest with yourself.

If you are struggling to get an honest answer from yourself, try asking yourself the following questions:

- Is my job really what I would like to do every day?
- Is this the relationship I want?
- Do I want to travel the world?
- Can I give back and contribute more to my world?
- Am I happy with how I treat myself?

Like a lot of personal questioning, this might not be an easy task and I would advise you to break up doing this exercise into small chunks so that you don't end up overwhelmed by it! But doing this honestly will show you what areas of your life are working for you, and which area you need to work on.

Be honest with yourself. This is your self-care and while you may have to face some home truths that you have swept under the carpet, doing this exercise lets you take control and implement change.

What I love about using the Wheel of Life tool is that gives you a visual impression of your life as a whole. It takes it out of your head, which can become cluttered with too many thoughts, and allows you to see on paper what's good and what you might improve on. It even allows you the opportunity to realise that some areas are not as bad as you thought! What you'll really grasp is an understanding of what you're doing and the areas you need to focus most on to help you find peace and balance.

THERE'S NO SUCH THING AS A BALANCED LIFE

'The truth is balance is bunk. It is an unattainable pipe dream. ... The quest for balance between work and life, as we've come to think of it, isn't just a losing proposition; it's a hurtful, destructive one.' **Keith H. Hammonds**

Does the thought of pursuing the dream of work–life balance add more pressure, stress and potential burnout to your life? Does not having a 'balanced life' add to your sense of failure? Do you see it as something else you haven't achieved, or another goal you haven't reached or have to work towards?

I have never really understood the term 'balanced life'. In fact, I would go so far as to say the term makes my skin crawl. The eternal pressure to have work–life balance. The idea that once you have found this elusive work–life balance, your total existence will suddenly be perfect. There is no such thing as a balanced life – it's a myth! Life is full of ups and down and unexpected twists and turns, which means it's not balanced. How can it be? If you are focused on something that is important, for however long or short a period of time, it means you are giving all your attention to that thing. Therefore, it means you have to take focus and maybe time away from other areas of your life in order to fulfil the needs of the main focus. Feeling that you should be giving the same amount of attention to each area of your life at any given moment is nothing short of pure madness. It is stressful and can and will only lead in one direction.

Think of balance as being in the middle of the line:

Out of balance ——————— Balanced life ——————————Out of balance

Let me explain:

- If your goal is to live a balanced life (in the middle), you are going to miss out on doing some pretty life-changing things for fear of putting yourself out of balance. You will shun anything that might throw your life off balance in the quest to live a balanced life.

- If your goal is **always** focused on work, you are going to miss out on your personal life. This is because you are always out of balance. You are constantly focused on just one area of your life. Maybe you think, 'I'll work really hard for the next X years and then I'll spend time going on holidays.' If you do this, your main focus is work and you are in an out-of-balance state, which can lead to burnout.

- Constantly trying to live a balanced life will drive you mad, not necessarily burnt-out, but the time and energy spent beating yourself up when you feel guilty about spending too much time focused on one area of your life is soul-destroying and can lead to low self-worth, which can contribute to burnout.

So what works instead of a striving for a balanced life? If you're like me, no matter how hard you try, there are always things you haven't ticked off your to-do list at the end of each day, week, month or year. Breathe — that is completely normal. This is what happens when you prioritise the important things; there will always be things that don't get done. Getting stressed about the things that haven't got done does not work towards creating a balanced life, neither does it result in healthy emotional thinking.

Let me explain. As I write this I have had a really busy week, which involved working 15-hour days. As good as my self-care is, and I can leave my work at my bedroom door, all I was able to do when I finished my work for the day was read a page or two of a book and then sleep. My week did not involve any down time, fun stuff or self-care. I have been totally focused on work and a project that is important to me, which means that other parts of my life are out of balance. In order to counterbalance this, next week, when I'm on holidays but I know I'll still have to work for the first few days, I'll get up early and run with my eldest son, I'll make a date with my youngest for breakfast, and I'll start work at 10 a.m. instead of 6 a.m. I'll aim to work two hours in the morning and three in the afternoon and spend the rest of each day with the boys, having fun and creating memories. A counterbalance to the previous week's busy work schedule has the opposite effect of working those long hours. In order for me to be able to do this, I had to identify beforehand that I was going to have a busy period of work and to counterbalance this by making time to do the things that are important to me.

Remember, there will always be periods in life when you will have to focus your time on something in particular that will mean time away from other things in your life. That is what causes imbalance. There are many reasons for this, perhaps a deadline at work, a wedding to plan, tax returns that have to be completed, or caring for an ill family member. In order to achieve things in life, you have to choose what is important to you at that time. This means that there will be an imbalance in other areas of your life – all those other things won't get done, and you won't have the time to spend on other areas of your life. This is the reality of life. However, for your self-care and to ensure you don't reach burnout, it's okay to focus on one area of your life for short periods of time. Just ensure that you remember to counterbalance it with the good stuff you enjoy.

For me, life is not about balance; it is about counterbalance. It's about knowing that when I'm working through a busy period, I have to counterbalance it with something that's equally important but has the opposite effect of work.

UNDERSTANDING YOUR ONE THING

In work and at home we all have goals, whether it is to get the house cleaned, complete a project in a certain time, buy a house or just get through the day. We generally live our lives by setting small or big goals that we have to achieve. What we don't do particularly well is having a system in which we get to our goal with as little stress as possible and without getting distracted by other things that pop into our day. And no matter how organised you are, life has a habit of throwing you curve balls when you least expect them, which puts pressure and stress on your current situation. What if you could find a system for both long- and short-term goals that will help alleviate the stress that confronts you when you have to deal with unforeseen added pressure?

Gary Keller and Jay Papasan wrote *The ONE Thing*, an extraordinary book that teaches you how to focus on identifying 'your one thing' that's important to you in the different areas of your life and how to work towards fulfilling your dream. If you're reading this thinking, 'But I've so many things I have to focus on and so many goals I have to achieve', you're right, you probably do. However, if you are, for example getting up each morning and seeing five different goals at work as 'your one thing', you are going to be putting yourself under a huge amount of stress trying to focus on each of them all the time in order to achieve them.

If I put you in a field and released five rabbits and told you to chase them, what do you think would happen? You'd be darting around the field like a lunatic, physically exhausted, emotionally frustrated and probably feeling like a failure at being unable to accomplish the task. That's what happens to you when you try to set too many unrealistic goals for yourself or, more important, when you have too many goals thrust upon you by others.

The principle of Keller and Papasan's 'Goal Setting in the Now' is that you can apply it to every area of your life. You can use it for setting long-term goals (like buying a house) in your personal life or simply use this system and apply it to short-term goals at work, at home or for your own personal self-care goal.

To give you the full picture of how this works, let's imagine your goal is going to night classes to learn a different skill set so that you can leave the job or career you absolutely hate and is a huge part of your daily stress.

First identify what it is you'd like to do.

- What is your dream job? (What, realistically, could you do with the rest of your life that would *fulfil* you?)
- Why do you want that job? (Is it status or because you know that it aligns with your values and beliefs, and what you are currently doing doesn't?)
- Now *visualise* yourself in this job.

Now that you have figured out 'your one thing' that you want to do with your career, start getting down to implementing your goal so that it doesn't add to your already busy life and cause more stress, which will lead to burnout and a sense of 'What's the point, I'm never going to have enough time to achieve my goal.'

Someday Goal (your dream job)

What's the ONE Thing I want to do someday?

Five-Year Goal

Based on my Someday Goal,

What's the ONE Thing I can do in the next five years?

One-Year Goal

Based on my Five-Year Goal,

What's the ONE Thing I can do this year?

Monthly Goal

Based on my One-Year Goal,

What's the ONE Thing I can do this month?

Weekly Goal

Based on my Monthly Goal,

What's the ONE Thing I can do this week?

Daily Goal

Based on my Weekly Goal,

What's the ONE Thing I can do today?

Right Now

Based on my Daily Goal,

What's the ONE Thing I can do right now?

That One Thing in your day, your week, your month and your year now becomes a non-negotiable. Maybe you don't have to go as far as adding a five-year goal because what you want can be achieved by only going as far at looking at your one-year goal. You identify the goal and work at putting this plan in place. Schedule time into your day, every day, that One Thing you can do to get to your goal. Put it in your diary as an appointment with yourself. If your goal is personal, maybe you need to schedule in the time to do it early in the morning or in the evening. If it's work-related, figure out a realistic time in the day you can dedicate to your One Thing. The time you spend on this is entirely up to you, but be realistic – scheduling four hours of time for your One Thing while you're already stretched to your limit won't be attainable. Maybe a more realistic 'right now' goal is 30 minutes or an hour. The point of doing this is that you're learning to train your mind to connect what you want to do (your goal) with what you can do right now to achieve your goal with the least amount of stress in your life.

Goal-setting in the now works by allowing you to be present in the now in order to work towards a future you want. Focusing purely on the end result can be overwhelming, it can allow your limiting self-beliefs to surface, cause unnecessary stress and possible burnout.

Using this exercise to work through goals in different areas of your life allows you to be in control of what you're doing, and it gives you the freedom to set realistic small goals to achieve your end game.

Having too many goals is like chasing five rabbits around a field and hoping to catch them all. Identifying your One Thing in different areas of your life allows you to work towards creating a life you want to live in rather than exist in. Regardless of the size of your goal, break your goals down into smaller chunks. Your One Thing is non-negotiable.

TIME MANAGEMENT

It sounds obvious, but time management is an essential part of reducing the possibility of burnout. How you spend your time, being smart about the hours you have gives you the control you need to end each day with a sense of positive wellbeing. We all have the same 24 hours in each day; it's how we choose to fill them that can cause us issues.

One definition of time management is, 'the ability to use one's time effectively or productively, especially at work'. Smart time management allows you to accomplish more in a shorter period of time, which in turn leads to more free time (to focus on your self-care) and reduces your stress. The benefits of time management are like a domino game; one hits off another and thus improves another aspect of your life.

Here are some ways to manage time and get your life back.

STOP MULTI-TASKING

I've already talked about why multi-tasking doesn't work. Nowadays I actively enjoy telling people, 'Sorry, I can only do one thing at once'; and while I still have friends who think multi-tasking is their only option, I am patiently waiting for the day they realise the damage it does to their brains and that single-tasking is the way forward! Multi-tasking, which was once seen as a badge of honour of how much work we could do, is not real, it is a myth. If your task is too big to complete in one sitting, then break it up into smaller tasks which you can accomplish individually without having or feeling the need to multi-task. If you've been a multi-tasker, I challenge you to change your badge and start being a single-tasker!

Doing things task by task is more efficient, and being more efficient means freeing up more time.

USE A DIARY OR PLANNER

I am for ever on the lookout for the perfect planner. I have shied away from using technology; as a visual person, I need to be able to see my week, month and year clearly laid out in black and white in front of me. In 2018 I found (after numerous purchases) the ideal planner – the Passion Planner (yes, I know the name is slightly off putting). It's an A4-size planner that breaks down each day into time slots. It also has a section each week for gratitude, random note writing, and other little surprises to help you keep planning on track. At the top of each day is a box for 'today's focus', which you use to make a note of your top priority that day (or your One Thing). For me the first thing that goes in is my self-care for that day – which might be training, a run or simply a quick walk. Next is my One Thing, which goes into a time slot every day. For a while my One Thing was writing this book. I scheduled into my day the time I would research and write, thus reducing the risk of stressing about getting to the end of the day without getting it done. Instead, putting it in as an appointment and seeing the time set aside means that I'm more inclined to get it done. I schedule in my private clients, the kids' appointments, work and personal meetings, food shopping (not the milk and bread runs, but the hour-plus weekly shop) and an hour for emergencies. That hour acts as a buffer for anything that crops up in my day that takes time away from the other things. Believe me, that hour is probably the most important part of my day. There are loads of amazing planners, but take it from someone who has done her research, the Passion Planner is by far the best.

DELEGATE

If you have too much on your plate that's causing you stress and not allowing you to get through your day, the magical art of delegating is one you should learn! Maybe delegating at work isn't something you feel comfortable about doing, or even able to do, so what about delegating at home instead? Sharing out tasks and giving others responsibilities may take a bit of time to organise, but the long-term payoff is more time for you. Feeling taken advantage of and unappreciated at home is as much a contributor to burnout as long-term stress at work. Delegate wherever you can, whether at work or at home.

LET IT GO: STOP TAKING ON TOO MUCH

Figure out what tasks you aren't great at. Be honest with yourself. Admitting you're not good at something might not be easy, but agreeing to do things that take up time you don't have means pushing the things you're good at down the list and will probably end up taking up too much time. Another way to start 'letting it go' is by looking at what tasks you truly enjoy completing and the ones you're especially good at. See 'letting go' as another form of decluttering – call it task decluttering.

THE IMPORTANCE OF ROUTINE

For some people, routine is a dirty word. It reminds them of boring days doing the same thing over and over. We seem to fear boredom and crave spontaneity and acting on impulse to inject excitement into our lives. But is that really the answer? We need to take the time to consider what's important to us or how we can turn our daydreams into goals we can actively work on. The problem is nearly always the same for all of us, we want to make changes to our lives, yet our commitments often end at good intentions. One way to make positive changes and stick with them is by creating a daily routine. A study by Philippa Lally at University College London found that it took, on average, 66 days for a new behaviour to become 'automatic', usually in the form of a habit. What was also comforting about the results of the study is the finding that 'Missing one opportunity to perform the behaviour did not materially affect the habit formation process.' There is no need to beat yourself up if things don't stay on track one day!

Decide that you want to make positive changes in your life. It's also important to be realistic and easy on yourself, so it may not be the best choice for you to try and start mindful meditation, digital detoxing and applying the 80/20 rules all in one day.

It's up to you to organise your own unique daily routine. That is the beauty of having a daily routine! You are in control and you are deciding what direction you want your life to go in. If you lead a stressful life and find time in the morning for gratitude practice and meditation, you are instantly enabling yourself to take on whatever the day ahead has to throw at you.

So how exactly do you start a daily routine? Identify what really matters to you, consider timeframes, be accountable to your routine and, most important, be adaptable. The last point is really important – even routines that nurture good habits need to be assessed. Just as children need and respond to routine, so do adults. With a good daily routine, good habits form, and we begin to make the changes we want to see in our lives. Therefore, rather than seeing routine as restrictive, see it as the vehicle that will take you on the journey to change. The benefits of having a structured daily routine far outweigh the negatives.

Week 7

Try a digital detox

F ollowing on from Week 6, when you looked at your time management, Week 7 is dedicated to doing a digital audit of the technology in your life. Looking at your phone, email, social media and television usage may unearth some thought-provoking facts about how you spend your time each day, week and month. This week has some interesting tips on how to reclaim precious time that you can now use to focus on your self-care.

TECHNOLOGY AUDIT

A huge part of the work I do around burnout involves discussing technology usage and the impact it has on so many areas of our lives. It is part of nearly every presentation and motivational talk I deliver. But just to be clear, when I refer to digital detox I do not mean throwing your phone away, or your laptop, TV, or any other technology that may be taking up too much time or even stressing you even more than you need. Technology is here to stay and is getting more advanced year by year, so this is not about living a technology-free life, it's about living smartly with technology so you're in control of it and it (and the impact it has on you) is not in control of you. I'm talking about reclaiming time, time that is yours and that is slipping through your fingers.

Technology habits that contribute to burnout are here to stay, so it is not about being tech-free but about being tech-smart!

SMARTPHONES

When working with clients who feel they don't have time to spend on themselves and their self-care, I ask them how much time, on average, they spend on their phones. The answers range from an hour a day to three or four hours, but as with most things in life we have a tendency to underestimate rather than overestimate!

In order to gain a greater understanding of your day-to-day phone usage I suggest monitoring it for a week. There are a few apps for android and iPhones that you can install on your phone to track your usage. My personal favourite is called Moment (only available on iPhone). According to Moment, we actually underestimate the amount of time we spend on our phones by 100%. That could add up to a huge amount of time every day that you could be dedicating to your self-care.

If you've read the section on multi-tasking, you'll already know that working on a project or task at work and idly flicking through your phone or using it to send emails while typing up a report is not actually helping you get through your workload any quicker; it's adding to your stress. This is what I refer to as a 'background stress'. Not a big, obvious one, but there nonetheless and therefore putting pressure on your adrenal glands and keeping you in a state of mild stress, for no good reason.

Obsessively checking our phones may look like addiction, but for most people it's a bad habit, boredom and a bizarre voyeuristic need to see what people we don't know are doing! These are behaviours that can be changed without severe or long-lasting withdrawal effects. Start to give yourself the freedom to have breaks from social media.

Having said this, a small proportion of people may be more prone to behavioural addictions to smartphone functions such as online gambling, pornography, games and social media. At the time of writing, you can't, clinically speaking, become addicted to a device, but you can develop behavioural addictions to smartphone functions. There is still extensive research being done to see what the long-term effects of phone usage are on our brains.

It may (or may not) interest you to know that Irish consumers use their smartphones an average of 57 times daily, with some heavy users admitting to checking their devices more than 100 times every single day, according to a study published by Deloitte – that is a lot of checking. Of the people who took part in the study, half actually believed they use their phones too much, while 60% thought their partners used their phone too much – that is a huge amount and increases the feelings of being disconnected. The research also reveals that 89% of people use their phones when in company, while 74% use their devices when in a restaurants or bars with family and friends. According to the research, 40% of Irish people look at their smartphones within five minutes of waking and three-quarters do so within half an hour. At the other end of the day, 30% said they checked their phone just before going to sleep.

PHONE DETOXING

First, ask yourself a few simple questions.

- Why exactly do you feel the need to have your phone in your hand, your pocket or attached to your hip most of the time?
- Do you take your phone to bed?
- How would you feel if you didn't take your phone to bed?
- Do you check your phone regularly?

- Have you set your social media apps to alert you when someone posts something?
- When you can't find your phone, does it send you into a tailspin?

Now that you've honestly answered these questions, let's look at what you can do to reduce your screen usage that might free up some of your time to do other things.

APPS

Yes, I am actually suggesting downloading another app. My current favourite is Moment. Moment is an 'invisible' app that helps you to be consciously aware of how much time you actually spend on your phone. It works quietly behind the scenes of your phone, keeping tabs on the time you spend with your phone open. The basic plan is enough to be able to track your daily screen usage, but there are lots of very smart extra features you can purchase that allow you to take control of your screen time. You can set your phone to have 'screen-free' time, and set daily limits for the amount of time you'd like to spend on your phone. This is easier to do once you've spent some time getting your stats sent via the Insights feature. Once you have an idea of how much time you spend in reality vs. your estimate, it's a good way to start reducing your time. There are even two 'courses' you can do via the app, Bored & Brilliant and Phone Bootcamp. Both are really engaging, funny and are not going to leave you feeling judged or, worse, bad about yourself and your screen usage! There are other similar apps available on other platforms, so you can try a few out. It's about taking control back in areas of your life that may, over time, have become habits that are perceived as being difficult to change.

On a side note to parents, if you have your face stuck in a screen, the chances are your kids will too! Set an example and create habits at home that everyone can live by.

PHONE BASKET

I have a basket in my hall where I leave my phones (I have two, one for work and one for personal stuff). The purpose of leaving my phones in the basket is twofold: (a) I don't lose them and (b) I don't have them in my back pocket as an added distraction from whatever I'm doing in the present moment. So if, for example, I'm cooking dinner and the phone rings, if it was in the kitchen with me or in my pocket, I might be tempted to answer the phone and attempt to multi-task, which I know doesn't work. I'm now either trying to cook and have a conversation, which means I end up doing neither particularly well – I don't pay attention to cooking and I'm not giving the person on the phone my full attention. I burn the dinner, which then gets delayed and causes me to feel stressed, I get annoyed with the caller and end up in a grumpy mood, all because I answered the phone. However, if I leave the phone in the basket while cooking the dinner and I hear it ring I can now make a conscious decision to stop what I am doing and go and answer it or I can simply continue doing what I'm doing (single-tasking!) and when I'm finished cooking I can return the call and give it my full attention.

PHONES IN BED

This is fairly simple. Do. Not. Bring. Your. Phone. To. Bed.

EMAIL

The ever-increasing need, or pressure, to feel connected to work has become an epidemic of the twenty-first-century working environment. I have clients who tell me they are expected to respond to emails after working hours, that checking emails after 9 p.m. can be the norm. **This is not normal!** (Unless, of course, you work for a company in another time zone.) Creating clear boundaries in work from the start is important. Start as you mean to continue. Use the out-of-office function on your email; activate it each evening as you leave work and most certainly on Friday evening. Stating when you will be out of the office and back in again gives colleagues the information they need about your whereabouts. It also sends a message that you are not actually contactable until the time and date you state. If you are reading this and thinking, 'Well, that's all very well in theory, but ...', it might be worth considering why you feel the need to be contactable in the first place. If you feel that activating the 'out-of-office' function will make colleagues think you are not pulling your weight, maybe you have deeper feelings of unworthiness. Feelings that you 'must' be contactable to show your commitment to the company. If you feel like this, it's important to ask yourself where that thought stems from. Setting boundaries might not be something that comes easily to you. You may not have had much opportunity to set clear boundaries personally, or perhaps you don't even know that you have the right to set healthy boundaries. If your limiting self-belief is not feeling worthy, even what seems like a simple task of setting boundaries around out-of-office contact may be challenging. Start setting small boundaries – you have the right to a personal life!

TV

In January 2017, after a Christmas break when the TV was on constantly, I created a new house rule. No TV Monday to Thursday! Yes, I was met with a child revolution, but I stuck with it and rode the wave of utter disbelief. If I was enforcing this ban on the boys, it also meant that I would abandon my nightly episodes of *CSI*; I would no longer be staring at the TV screen at 1 a.m. under the illusion that I was having 'me' time. Suddenly I had three, yes three, more hours every night to do stuff I cared about, and that included going to bed earlier and reading a book. By July 2017 I called the TV provider and cancelled my TV subscription. I kept my broadband, but I now no longer had channel surfing at my fingertips. The boys found they had more time at the weekends to do things they cared about, and they also learned how to be bored, which in turn has taught them as young teenagers to be a bit more creative in their thinking and doing. Letting go of having hundreds of stations to watch allows you to reclaim time you didn't think you had. Yes, spending time as a family watching a movie is great social connection and as I have broadband and our TV has Netflix, we still have movie nights at the weekends. At Christmas myself and my younger son spent an entire day watching back-to-back episodes of *Stranger Things* and it was fabulous. We planned the day from start to finish and it's a memory we will both have for a very long time. I totally disconnected from all other parenting duties, my work phone was switched off and I was utterly present in the moment with him. Mindful TV watching! Having a TV in your bedroom is just another distraction from switching off and getting good sleep. I'm not suggesting you get rid of your TV or follow my lead and ban the TV, but be mindful of the amount of time you spend watching stuff you don't really have any interest in. Using that time to go for a walk or cook something nutritious to eat, even getting to bed an hour earlier, are all self-care practices that support your emotional and physical resilience.

Taking back screen time is going to allow you to get to bed earlier, get to sleep easier, find time to exercise, focus on sitting down to eat rather than scrolling, practise single-tasking and maybe even improve your relationships!

Week 8

Thoughts, feelings and words: how they affect you

Week 8 explores how your thoughts, feelings and words affect you and how you interact in the world. Using the principles behind cognitive behavioural therapy, there are exercises to help you see how negative or unhelpful thoughts can impact on how you feel and behave, which can lead to burnout. Understanding how this cycle works lets you figure out if you're reacting to situations from real facts or assumptions based on hypothetical thoughts. This week also covers how you can strive to be 10% happier in your life and what being congruent to yourself means. Using the non-negotiables you established in Week 6, you can work through the exercise on how to determine what your personal values and beliefs are and how they relate to your self-care.

COGNITIVE BEHAVIOURAL THERAPY

In my client work, one of the main therapies I use is cognitive behavioural therapy (CBT). I look at how people currently think, feel and behave in their lives. Allowing clients the opportunity to see how their thoughts really influence how they think and behave is a powerful tool in being able to help them make the changes they need. We have a tendency to base a lot of our behaviour on thoughts that are not based on fact but on imagined scenarios we think might happen. This can cause us to get into a pattern of negative automatic thought processing, which means that we can behave in a way that damages us in how we view and act in our world. CBT is a practical way of challenging our negative automatic thought processing in a way that helps promote change.

CBT challenges you to look at how you think (cognitive) about yourself, the world you live in and the people around you, and how what you do (behaviour) affects your thoughts and feelings. Knowing how you think about yourself is key to being able to shift your behaviours so that you don't end up burnt-out.

CBT focuses on 'here and now' problems and difficulties, which is why it is such a good tool to know how to use when you are experiencing symptoms of burnout. If I were working with a client in real time, I would probably discuss their past behaviours and understand how their lives to date have influenced their current situation, but for now the focus is on improving your mental wellbeing *now*.

CBT says that it's not the event that causes our emotions, but how we interpret that event – what we think or what meaning we give that event or situation. To break this down into a relatable example, imagine that someone you know passes you in the street without acknowledging you. You can interpret this in several different ways. If your self-worth is low, your automatic negative thought might be that they don't want to say hello to you because they (and everyone else) don't like you (which may lead you to *feeling* depressed and isolated). Your thought might be that you hope they don't stop to talk to you, because you won't know what to say to them and they'll think you're boring and stupid (this could make you feel *anxious*). You might even think they're intentionally ignoring you (leading to feeling *angry*, *upset* and *hurt*). All of these examples are thoughts, simply thoughts, not facts – it is our negative automatic thought process working at full speed. When we allow these thoughts to influence us, they can create unhealthy feelings, which influence how we behave. A healthier response might be that they just didn't see you. They may have been lost in their own thoughts, have heard upsetting news, or even had similar thoughts to your own.

Using CBT can help you to break these cycles of negative thinking, feelings and behaviour, which I'm going to break down into easy-to-understand exercises.

As I said, I would normally work with clients directly first to get them to understand how CBT works and get them to do 'homework', which we would discuss at their sessions, but the aim of this book is to get you to a point where you can do it yourself, and work out your own ways of tackling problems.

If you are unsure you're doing it 'right' or would like to have some structured guidance, I suggest finding a CBT therapist and booking a few sessions to clear up any uncertainty you may have.

Now let's look at what is helping to keep *your* problems alive, which could be adding to your burnout.

IDENTIFYING THOUGHTS, FEELINGS AND BEHAVIOURS

Think of a recent example of when you've been stressed, something that has happened in the past few weeks, a time when you've felt particularly anxious, angry or overwhelmed.

Write it down on paper and break it down into smaller chunks of information. You can use this template to start with.

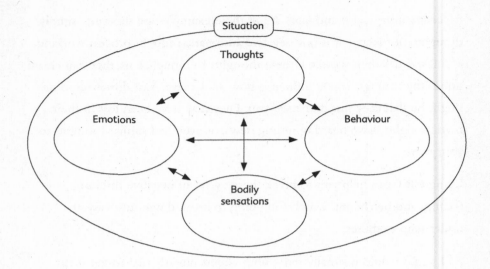

● What was the **situation**? What happened? When did it happen? What else was going on for you at the time? Was it a situation that you often find yourself in? Who were you with?

Now ask yourself:

● What **thoughts** went through your mind just before or during that time? What annoyed you? What did that thought mean to you, or what did that thought say about you or the situation?

● What negative **emotions** did you feel? (Examples of negative emotions would be anger, anxiety, rage, depression, frustration, guilt, shame, irritability.)

● What did you notice in your **body**? (Did you feel your heart pounding, or palpitations, did your breathing increase, or maybe you suddenly had difficulty concentrating?)

Now here's the interesting bit – the **behaviour**.

● What did you do? What didn't you do? How did you cope?

Most people have 'go-to' behaviours they unconsciously revert to when they are in a negative automatic thought process. Here are some of the negative behaviours that different emotions can cause. Can you identify with any of them?

- **Anxiety/low self-worth.** Stayed at home, left wherever you were or felt the urge to leave, withdrew from conversations, avoided eye contact, didn't go out, distracted yourself (TV, radio, kept busy, etc.), drank more, smoked more, ate more (or less), disturbed sleep.

- **Anger.** Shouted at someone, had a go at someone, sulked, criticised others (or had the urge to do those things), bottled it up, lost control.

Having done this exercise, what have you noticed about your thought processing?

Write down at least one situation every day for the next few days and see if you notice a pattern.

> Practise noticing your thoughts, feelings and behaviours. The more you practise, the more you will notice them. The more you notice them, the more easily you will be able to change behaviours that are not helpful to you.

Now that you've identified how your thoughts might not be based on truth or facts, it's time to change them!

FACT OR OPINION?

When we are stressed, we have a tendency to focus on what's not working for us rather than what is. Our rational thinking takes a back seat and our ability to respond to situations is compromised. We let our imagination take over and create thoughts based on no facts whatsoever, and we let our mind get ruled by our personal opinions. This then impacts on our feelings (emotions) and results in behaviours being driven by emotions and opinions rather than facts.

Fact	Opinion
Evidence-based information	Personal belief
Definite	Emotion
Rational thought	Fear

If you look back at the example of the friend passing you on the street and not acknowledging you and the different thoughts you might have had – based on opinions, not facts – it's easy to see how easily we can react to situations in a way that ends up causing us more stress. Jumping to conclusions is not helpful and only causes stress.

PAM'S STORY

A client recently came to me with a similar situation – a leaving party for one of her work colleagues. My client used to work in this colleague's department, but because of a work restructure in the company she is now situated on her own in the building and is not part of any department as such. On the day in question, she came to me very upset, angry and stressed as she found out that she hadn't been invited to the party. This only compounded the stress she had already from the work restructure. She felt picked on, excluded and alienated by this recent event. She felt she had been deliberately excluded because she no longer worked in the same department. She didn't want to go into work and her stress regarding the restructure of her job was increased. All her feelings about the situation were based on her thoughts, which were purely based on opinion rather than fact. In our session I asked her to start by writing down the situation and how she thought, felt and behaved. Doing this, even though she had talked it through with me, allowed her to fully see on paper how she reacted to the situation. Next, I asked her to write down the facts behind how she felt. What was the evidence behind her feeling picked on, excluded and alienated? What were the specific facts backing up her feelings? Once she had time to think about the facts she realised she didn't have any! Her feelings were based on personal opinions and emotions. With a new perspective on the situation, we discussed what she could do differently that would change her behaviour. We discussed the possibility that she might approach one of her colleagues whom she knew well and simply ask if everyone was invited or not. Yes, she would be putting herself out there, but she would also then have facts rather than opinion to base her feelings and her behaviours on. We role played how she could approach the situation a few times, and the following day, Pam spoke to her colleague and explained how she felt. The reality of the situation was very different to what Pam thought. It had been an oversight due to the fact that Pam was no longer based in the department. She had been included in the restaurant booking, as she would normally have been, and her colleagues had assumed that Pam would take it as a given that she was invited. In working through her negative automatic thought processing, Pam was able to change how she felt about a situation that could have impacted her negatively.

At stressful times, we tend to be driven by our emotions and opinions, which create a vicious cycle by fuelling each other. Our emotions strengthen our opinions, which in turn intensify our emotions. This leads to impulsive acts and unhelpful longer-term consequences, which help to maintain the overall problem.

It can therefore be helpful to ask ourselves whether what we're thinking is *fact* or *opinion*. If it's a fact, we can make choices about what we can or cannot do. If it's an opinion, we can look at the facts – what do we **know** about the situation?

> Negative automatic thought processing can lead to negative feelings and behaviours. Question your thoughts and check if they are based on facts or your opinion. Use the CBT model to work through and understand your own thought-processing behaviours.

LANGUAGE PATTERNS

'Our life is shaped by our mind; we become what we think.' **Buddha**

How we speak to others and to ourselves has a direct impact on our thoughts and feelings and ultimately our behaviours. As someone who loves weight training, if I say to myself ,'I *can't* lift 100 kilo deadlift', the chances are that not only will I not be able to do it there and then, but I'm sending a direct message to my brain that I will never be able to do it. If I rephrase it to, 'I'm currently not able to lift 100 kilo deadlift but I'm working on increasing my strength to be able to', I'm now sending a message to my brain that this is something I am able to achieve. Equally, if I say, 'I'm going to *try* to lose weight, give up smoking, or leave the office earlier', the chances are that I won't. By saying *try* we are sending a signal to our brains that (a) we really aren't that bothered or (b) we're already setting ourselves up for failure. If I say 'I *am* going to lose weight, give up smoking, or leave the office earlier', I am telling my brain that I am going to action a task. With a simple switch in my language pattern, I am going from inaction and possible failure to action and enthusiasm about achieving it.

Using positive language is one of the simplest exercises you can do to change your thoughts and feelings. It really is as simple as changing the words you use. Think of this as more than just a simple exercise, think of it as a whole new way of life.

This is an exercise you can start right this very second and begin to notice results immediately. However, breaking old habits takes time and awareness. You will have to:

1. Become aware of the words you use and how they affect your thoughts, feelings and actions.

2. When you find yourself using words that are not encouraging you, correct yourself mentally and replace them with positive empowering words.

3. Eventually break the habit of using negative words and naturally speak and think using your new pattern of language and thought.

4. Take a few minutes to think about how the people around you speak and imagine why they speak the way they do and what effects this might have on them.

5. Imagine the choice of words that a doctor might use, both positive and negative words, and picture how their choice of words may make their patients feel.

6. Imagine the words an old schoolteacher might use in the classroom and how their choice of words might impact on the children they teach.

This may seem very simple to you, almost too simple to be of any real use. But like a lot of the self-care tools I utilise, sometimes it's the smallest and simplest tools that have the biggest impact on our lives.

There are literally hundreds of negative words in the English language, but we'll focus on a few of the most common ones. Begin to understand how each word affects how you feel.

First, think of some of the words you might currently use and the effect those words have on you, what they make you think, the emotions that follow and how those emotions make you think.

For example, let's take the word 'anxious'. There are people who suffer crippling anxiety, and I am by no means belittling how they feel. However, on a more general level, the word 'anxious' is used to describe a whole host of emotions that might easily be managed by reframing the words you use. Replace the word 'anxious' with 'concerned' and you send your brain a very different message. Replace the word 'failure' with 'feedback' and 'can't' with 'choosing' and you remove the negativity from your life experiences. If you use the word 'depressed' when in fact you are simply 'fed up', you are sending your brain a very powerful message which will in turn effect your thoughts, the chemical reactions in your brain and your emotions, which will change how you think, feel and behave.

Changing negative language to positive language and reprogramming yourself to think and feel good is a tool that affects not only you but also those around you. Starting now, throw out the negative words and focus on their positive replacements.

Remember, there is no such thing as a negative occurrence in life. It's only your interpretation of it that makes it negative. With a positive outlook on life, what may initially seem to be something bad will turn into something good if you believe it will. Something positive can be taken from any situation if you choose to recognise it.

POSITIVE PSYCHOLOGY: 10% HAPPIER

Over the years the practice of psychology has been criticised for focusing more on the negative traits of people's personalities than on the positive elements of human potential. Positive psychology promotes the importance of positivity in our everyday lives.

One of the most effective ways to practise positive psychology is through affirmations. Affirmations are statements that we say or think repeatedly. They can be positive or negative, and when we repeat them daily, they can transform and shape our lives for good or bad. You may not consider yourself to be a negative person, but every complaint, every internal moan about a colleague, friend or family member, every criticism of your personal abilities is an affirmation.

To harness the power of affirmations, use journalling to stop saying negative things so that you can start repeating and creating new positive and empowering statements like 'I deserve to be happy' and 'I am loved'. Whether or not the statements you decide to repeat are true, they'll motivate you, keep your mind focused on a goal and start to retrain your way of thinking.

Write your positive affirmations in your journal and say them out loud daily. This increases their effectiveness, reprogramming your mind and increasing the likelihood that you will believe and act upon them.

It really is possible to become happier and more fulfilled – and you can start with simple, positive words!

BEING CONGRUENT

Being congruent means living a life that aligns with your personal values and beliefs.

> 'Your beliefs become your thoughts. Your thoughts become your words. Your words become your actions. Your actions become your habits. Your habits become your values. Your values become your destiny.' **Mahatma Gandhi**

Living your life being congruent with yourself is one of the most important ways to live a successful, happy life. Success is not measured by how much money you have in the bank or what car you drive; it is the personal success of feeling content that you are living by your own set of personal values and beliefs. Your values are a set of attitudes, unique to you, that control your behaviour (and that we pass on to the next generation) and influence the way we exist in the world.

Each and every one of us is striving to achieve different goals in life, and how you view your values is what allows you to achieve these goals. If your values don't align with the way you are living your life, you are going to feel, over time, resentful, angry, unhappy, apathetic, with low self-worth, and all the other negative symptoms of burnout. Living a life being congruent with your values is essential because it is what determines what means most to you.

To give you an example, I see my life with my boys and extended family as the most important value to me. I believe that spending time with my family is more important than working long hours. When I allow work to become more important (sometimes work gets busy and family gets temporarily pushed to the side) it makes me feel somewhat stressed. I am not stressed about my workload because I love my work, but my value system is out of alignment and I am not being congruent with my values and beliefs.

Knowing your personal values can help you prioritise what's important in your life and start to live a more congruent life.

Another way to explain personal values is to look at how marketers and advertising agencies use values to sell products. 'Caring for people and planet', 'Togetherness' and 'Cost conscious' are just three of the values that are part of the Ikea company. These values are aligned with how the company works for both customers and staff and it is what we expect from Ikea. We can see how the company uses these values in its advertising campaigns, family offers and the in-store events it holds.

Personal values are the essence of who you are. Your personal values and beliefs may be very different from the ones you were raised with or they may very well still be the same, but whatever they are, they are the core of what motivates you to be your best.

Thankfully, everyone is unique. We all have little quirks that make us who we are, and the more we understand ourselves, through working through some of the exercises in this book, the more self-aware we become and the easier it is to live a successful (content) life.

The process of discovering your personal values involves not just discovering what is important to you, but also finding out what you are really passionate about. For example, 'learning' is one of my personal values. It's important for me to be constantly learning in life; maybe this has to do with not completing school, but whatever the motivation behind it means that I am always eager to learn. I'm also a 'doer', so being productive and achieving personal goals is also important to me, and if I look back at the last ten years, I have been true to my values and have learned so many different skills and am still constantly learning. I use my personal values and beliefs to guide me in what I should do in life.

CREATING YOUR OWN PERSONAL VALUE SYSTEM

I believe that we should frequently ask ourselves what things are important to us and we should live our lives according to those things. There are always going to be things we don't want to do, but if we have a strong value system we can strive to live our lives, to the best of our ability, aligned with our personal values.

If we don't know what's important to us, how can we take personal responsibility for how we live our lives?

If you're not truly aware of your personal values, it becomes all too easy to slip into a life of existence rather than living. Basically, if you don't take control of your life, someone else will. And when that happens it all too easy to see how burnout can creep up on you.

Another reason why knowing what your personal values are is important is because it then becomes clear to us when we are experiencing a 'values conflict' and to understand rationally why and how we feel conflicted. Truly understanding what your personal values are allows you to eliminate feeling frustrated or angry about a situation.

Let's look at my example of my personal value of 'family'. When I am going through a busy work period I experience a value conflict when I feel like my 'family' value is being compromised. But rather than feel guilty about not spending time with them or feeling resentful at being busy with my workload, I am now aware that my personal value is being conflicted and I'm not actually guilty or resentful. I've learned how to manage myself in dealing with the conflict until my value system is restored to normal. Sometimes, just understanding why we feel frustrated can help us move forward without feeling stressed or letting our inner critic raise its ugly head.

Another example of 'values conflict' is when we are living a life according to someone else's values. This is very common when working for a company whose values don't align with yours; or it can even come from your own family. As I said earlier, our personal values can come from how we were raised. Often children will pick up their parents' values instead of their own and carry them into their adult life. As a child you may have been pushed into a college education or career you didn't really place any value on: your parents may have thought education was a personal value of theirs that should be important to you; you, on the other hand, may have thought travelling was an important value. You can never be happy when caught in the middle of a 'values conflict'.

If you take the time to identify your values, they will become your own personal framework for your self-care.

Identifying your personal values is like writing a personal mission statement. It signifies what is truly important to you and by what standards you want to live your life. It also allows you to see what is not important and to work at spending less time getting caught up living your life through other people's values and beliefs.

Using the list of words in the table opposite, circle the ones that resonate with you. It doesn't matter how many of them you circle, the exercise is to get you to focus on words that mean something to you.

Once you've identified the words you like, write them down on a separate sheet of paper and spend some time thinking about what they mean to you. You might add to this list, change some words or take some away.

Underneath each of the words you have chosen, write down why it is important to you. If 'family' is one of your words, describe why you've chosen it and what it means to you. Do this for all the words on your list. This is now your list of personal values and beliefs. Use these values as part of your self-care essentials and work at living your life by them. Refer to the list regularly and change your values if you feel you need to, but use the same steps as above when you do.

Remember, it's okay to have different values from other people; what is important is knowing what your values are.

PERSONAL VALUES

Week 9

Self-care, self-love and self-esteem

T he aim, by Week 9, is to have a greater level of knowing how you can take control of yourself and how you interact with the world. This week is about your self-care. It's about learning how incredibly important how you view yourself is to how you interact and connect with others and how your self-compassion is a necessary part of your recovery. Knowing the difference between self-esteem and self-confidence, and which one to focus on first, can be the light bulb moment in which you realise how to start learning self-love. This is a lovely part of the 12-week programme and one not to be underestimated.

Self-care is like the safety announcement on aeroplanes around the world: 'In the event of a drop in cabin pressure, an oxygen mask will drop from above. Please put your own mask on first before attending to others.' Think about it. The purpose of this announcement is not only to protect your own safety but to ensure that once you have attended to your own needs, you will be in a better position to attend to others who may need your help. Self-care is just like that. If you do not attend to your own self-care first, you are not in a position to help others. You will burn out and end up unable to help yourself and others.

Years ago, when I was doing my training to become a psychotherapist, we would have a day every month for self-reflection. During these day-long sessions our lecturer would talk about self-care. She was a beautiful, calm lady who would tell us the importance of making our self-care a priority. At this point in my life I was a single parent, my boys were three and four years old, and this lovely lady was telling me to take the time to meditate and reflect daily. One day she suggested that we all have a chair in our homes and we should tell our families that when we were sitting in it, we were not to be disturbed. I fell around the room laughing! How on earth was I going to tell two small children that when I sat in this chair, I was having 'me-time'? I couldn't even go to the toilet on my own, let alone sit in a chair being mindful. To me at the time, the notion of self-care was only for those who already lived calm, stress-free lives, not for those whose lives were a constant bundle of playing catch-up and organised chaos. Roll on eight years and my life is still a wonderful bundle of playing catch-up and organised chaos, and I still don't have a 'mindfulness' chair, but I have learned how to incorporate my self-care into my world so that it doesn't involve sitting in a chair telling two boys they can't talk to me! I have a lovely sofa in my office which I sometimes sit in and have a mini 'life-pause', and oftentimes I will find my younger son lying on the sofa enjoying a few minutes of peace and solitude!

The word 'wellness' has become commonplace in schools, colleges and workplaces around the world. Buzz words like self-care, mindfulness, gratitude, journalling and visualisation are thrown around like confetti and I feel sometimes they can add to feelings of stress rather than relieve it. The misconception that you have to spend hours every day to practise self-care can stop you actually doing anything for yourself.

With clients every day I hear:

- But I don't have time!

- I'll do it when I'm not busy at work.

- I'll start when the kids are older.

- I can't get up any earlier than I already do!

- I've nowhere to go to meditate, 'they' follow me everywhere!

I've even had clients who thought, 'All that self-care stuff, that's just mumbo-jumbo nonsense for people who don't have anything better to do!' I thought the same way once, but I'm here to tell you that it's not mumbo-jumbo and that self-care is *the* most important thing you can do for yourself. It is the core and foundation of living a healthier life physically, emotionally and, some would say, spiritually; it is the energy you hold within yourself and project around you. It is your personal blanket that protects you from burnout. No one else can do it for you and the sooner you realise that, the better!

Can you identify with any of these statements?

- I go to bed exhausted and wake up exhausted.

- I struggle focusing and completing tasks due to low energy.

- Most of the time I walk around feeling like four of the seven dwarves – Sleepy, Dopey, Grumpy and Sneezy.

- The closest I come to exercising is brushing my teeth or walking to the car.

- I can't find time in my busy day to eat lunch, yet I drink numerous cups of coffee during the day just to keep going.

- As a result of all that caffeine, I'm a bundle of nerves.

- I find myself doing things for others, with little or no time for myself.

- I keep thinking, next week, next week I'll mind myself.

Can you relate to the above list? All joking aside, if you're walking around feeling exhausted or low in energy, it's a sign that your self-care is in need of attention.

If you don't take care of yourself, who will? Neglecting yourself to meet others' needs can negatively impact your physical, emotional and mental health. As you now know, not getting enough sleep can result in feelings of exhaustion, difficulty concentrating, increased stress and irritability. Over time, the stress might settle in your shoulders, neck and back, creating physical pain like backaches or headaches. Your appetite might be affected, causing you to eat too much or too little. Under stress, along with the cortisol and glucose, the brain can release a lot more acid, which can lead to feelings of nausea or heartburn. The reality is that your body is like a car: you wouldn't drive it with no oil or water and expect it to perform at peak standards!

Emotional stress is often linked to stressful thoughts. This combination can have a detrimental effect on your level of energy, mental clarity and emotions.

SARAH'S STORY

Sarah was stressed and overwhelmed by the things that were happening in her life. Her mother was ill and needed a lot of care. She was also going through the break-up of a long-term relationship and had just started a new job. She was on an emotional rollercoaster, and had a constant throbbing headache. She felt utterly overwhelmed and her ability to concentrate and perform at work was seriously affected. Pressure, internally and externally, was mounting, and she felt something was about to snap.

One morning, when she was driving, she was so overwhelmed by her thoughts that she didn't notice a red light and ended up rear-ending another car. Thankfully, no one was seriously injured. However, it was the catalyst for her to realise she needed to make some changes to her life. It was at this point that she started attending sessions with me, and with some outside help she was able to identify how important her own self-care was in order to be able to manage all that was going on in her life. She couldn't run away from herself, so she needed to build up her self-care and personal resilience.

Continually putting your own needs last can create feelings of resentment and anger and can hurt close relationships personally and professionally. You may feel as if others are taking advantage of you or taking you for granted. You may be angry with yourself for not setting boundaries, or setting boundaries and not keeping to them. Mentally beating yourself up or resenting others doesn't change how you feel; it doesn't make anything any better. What does help is learning how to value yourself just as much as you value others. And I know this can be a challenging task – it's taken me a very long time to get it!

So what stops you practising self-care? There are many reasons you may struggle with putting yourself first, for example:

- being a carer to a sick family member or child
- a belief that focusing on self-care is selfish (the most common reason I hear every day)
- limiting self-beliefs
- religious beliefs that you must always put others first
- beliefs carried over from childhood, when caring for others' needs was a way to gain attention, approval and love.

You may relate to the above reasons or have reasons of your own. While it may take time to change a pattern or find support to help care for a sick family member, for example, it is important to take a break and mind yourself. Attending to your own needs helps keep your physical and emotional energy in a good place so that you are able to help others.

Practical ways to incorporate self-care into your daily routine:

○ Start the day by taking time to meditate. Notice what you feel in your body, tune in to your breathing, and acknowledge thoughts without focusing on any particular thought or story. A simple two-minute breathing exercise before you even get out of bed can really impact your day.

○ Make a list of the things that made you happy when you were young. Choose one and do it!

○ Schedule a play date for yourself. Don't wait for someone to be around to do things with, go and see a movie on your own, start a class, go to a museum. Whatever it is that makes you smile, do it!

○ If you can, join a yoga class and learn to relax your mind and flow with movement. Sometimes being part of a group can help you learn how to relax.

○ Practise mindful walking in a park and focus on your surroundings. Connect with the natural beauty that surrounds you. Notice the following: is it a sunny day? What are the colours around you? Are there birds singing? Week 11 is dedicated to understanding mindfulness, the benefits of daily practice and ways of making it part of your life rather than having to find extra time to practise it.

○ Practise assertiveness by learning how to say no! Start with the small stuff.

○ Delegate. Let go of having to do it all yourself. Ask for support. Allow others to help you and themselves.

○ If you're feeling overwhelmed or sad, call a friend and ask for support. If you just need someone to listen, ask for that.

○ Seek professional help from either your GP, life coach or a psychotherapist. If you are stuck with how to start minding yourself and implement the changes you know you want to, it can help to share your feelings and thoughts in a non-judgemental and compassionate setting.

◐ Work through your negotiables and non-negotiables. Let go of obligations that you don't need to keep and focus on the non-negotiables.

Remember, take time to shift from getting things done and feeling exhausted to creating a life that works for you. Choose one activity from this list and put it at the top of your self-care plan or create your own plan. The important thing is making time to take care of yourself.

When you listen and connect to what is going on in your body, mind and heart, you can start to take the first steps towards putting yourself first and minding your self-care. It is then, when you identify your needs and make time to nurture yourself, that you open the door to living your life.

Self-care safety announcement: 'In the event of a drop in cabin pressure, an oxygen mask will drop from above. Please put your own mask on first before attending to others.'

SELF-ESTEEM VS. SELF-CONFIDENCE

Before we go any further, I want to look at self-esteem and self-confidence and explain how confusing them, or thinking they are one and the same, can hinder your self-care.

I regularly see clients who don't understand the difference between self-esteem and self-confidence. In fact a lot of people think that self-confidence and self-esteem are the same, but they are actually very different. Imagine that self-confidence is on the outside and self-esteem is on the inside. I've worked with many clients who display great confidence on the outside – they're good at their jobs, are loyal friends, can even stand up in front of hundreds of people and deliver outstanding presentations – yet on the inside they have little or no self-esteem.

First I will explain the differences between self-esteem and self-confidence, then I'll look at what *you* can do to help improve your self-esteem and self-confidence.

Let's look at confidence. This comes from a place of knowledge and practice. The more experience you have in what you do, the more confident you will become. Remember back to when you first started driving. You were unsure of yourself and your ability and probably lacked a certain amount of confidence in your driving ability. The more you practised driving, the better you became until you got to a point where you could describe yourself as a confident driver. Take this a step further and self-confidence is about trusting yourself and your ability to succeed at new challenges, tasks and opportunities in life.

Take a minute to write down three things you have done where the more you practised, the better you were at doing it.

1. _____

2. _____

3. _____

For example, if you have to give presentations in work, the more you do them, the better you get at doing them; the more your knowledge of your subject matter allows you to act from a place of confidence in delivering the presentation, the more you will learn and the better you will be at delivering them.

The more your knowledge and practice is increased, the more you build your confidence.

It is also possible to be confident in some areas of your life and not in others. For example, I am confident in my public speaking abilities but not in my experience or knowledge of accountancy.

The problem with confusing self-confidence and self-esteem with each other is that if you focus on self-confidence (outside influence) to define who you are, instead of working on your self-esteem (inner self-care), you will rely on your achievements to make you feel good about yourself. If you only depend on achievements to make you feel good, the danger is that you can get into a spiral of depending on accomplishments to make you feel confident. Depending purely on accomplishments is exhausting, and it can lead to feelings of low self-esteem when new challenges have not been conquered.

It's very easy to slip into a pattern of defining yourself by what you do rather than who you are!

Psychiatrist Neel Burton explains: 'People usually find it easier to build their self-confidence than their self-esteem, and, confusing one with the other, end up with a long list of abilities and achievements. Rather than facing up to their imperfections and failures, they hide them behind their certificates and prizes. But a long list of abilities and achievements is neither sufficient nor necessary for healthy self-esteem. While people keep on working on their list in the hope that it might one day be long enough, they try to fill the emptiness inside them with status, income, possessions, relationships, sex, and so on.'

Self-esteem is how we view who we are irrespective of what we do. If, for example, I don't get the job I've applied for, I don't interpret that as 'I am a failure therefore I'm a bad person.' I'm able to rationalise that maybe the job wasn't for me or I may need to practise my interview skills. I'm still a good person and not getting the job does not reflect on who I am on the inside. It merely makes me focus on how I can increase my knowledge and practise to ensure I am better at interviews.

Self-esteem is about how you feel about yourself and how you value your worth. It is the essence of how we think, feel and behave. Much of our self-esteem is connected to the relationships we have and the people we surround ourselves with. Like attracts like and surrounding yourself with people who are positive can help build your self-esteem and your belief in yourself. Your self-esteem is what motivates you to learn more, seek new opportunities and connect with others.

People with healthy self-esteem also do not feel the need to rely on achievements to define who and what they are; they are content with knowing their value and their worth outside their self-confidence.

I constantly tell my clients, 'Don't keep going back to people who are going to talk negative to you. Surround yourself with people who are positive and who motivate you to want to be the best you can be for you, not people who make you feel inadequate in who you are or what you do.'

Want to fine-tune your self-esteem? Pick one of these things and practise it daily for a month. Then add another in and continue until these practices become as habitual as brushing your teeth.

- **Improve your self-talk.** Start your day with a positive intention and learn to refocus your thoughts to working for you, not against you.

- **Surround yourself with positive people.** Don't let negative people control the way you think about your life or your work. Remember, every negative person has a problem for every solution. Think about it and move on!

- **Start a journal.** Start a journal to share your thoughts and challenges. Be sure to focus on writing about the good things and not just the bad things. When you are having a down day, read back over the good things that happened and what behaviours you applied to your life to feel good. Focus, and repeat those same habits.

◗ **Get over your perfectionism.** Perfectionism stops us moving forward and completing projects. It paralyses us because we are so afraid of not being able to live up to our own high standards. Re-read Week 4.

◗ **Handle mistakes and failures in a more positive way.** I like to use this example when I talk about failure. Imagine you're driving your car, using Google Maps to direct you, and you take a wrong turn. Google Maps does not say, 'You've made a mistake. Give up and go home.' It simply recalculates, finds a different route, and gets you back on track. When you make a mistake or view something as a failing in life, reframe it and view it as taking a wrong turn, recalculate and move on.

◗ **Love others.** When you spend time being more kind and loving to others, you start to learn to treat yourself a little kinder too. Be encouraging to others, do a good deed or just be a great listener to someone.

SELF-WORTH QUIZ

This quiz from the University of Wisconsin (wire.wisc.edu) lets you get an idea of how you feel about your self-worth.

1. I generally feel pretty good about myself as a person.				
Strongly disagree	Disagree Somewhat	Neither Agree nor Disagree	Agree Somewhat	Strongly Agree
1	2	3	4	5

2. Most people I know are more intelligent and capable than I am.				
Strongly disagree	Disagree Somewhat	Neither Agree nor Disagree	Agree Somewhat	Strongly Agree
1	2	3	4	5

3. Most people I know are more attractive than I am.

Strongly disagree	Disagree Somewhat	Neither Agree nor Disagree	Agree Somewhat	Strongly Agree
1	2	3	4	5

4. Most people I know are more interesting than I am.

Strongly disagree	Disagree Somewhat	Neither Agree nor Disagree	Agree Somewhat	Strongly Agree
1	2	3	4	5

5. I am often surprised to find out that other people see me more positively (e.g. as more intelligent, attractive, competent) than I see myself.

Strongly disagree	Disagree Somewhat	Neither Agree nor Disagree	Agree Somewhat	Strongly Agree
1	2	3	4	5

6. I feel like I am a pretty good catch as a relationship partner.

Strongly disagree	Disagree Somewhat	Neither Agree nor Disagree	Agree Somewhat	Strongly Agree
1	2	3	4	5

7. When I complete a challenging task it generally makes me feel good about myself.

Strongly disagree	Disagree Somewhat	Neither Agree nor Disagree	Agree Somewhat	Strongly Agree
1	2	3	4	5

8. How I feel about myself is determined to a large extent by what I think others think of me.

Strongly disagree	Disagree Somewhat	Neither Agree nor Disagree	Agree Somewhat	Strongly Agree
1	2	3	4	5

9. I often find myself thinking negative thoughts about myself (e.g. 'I am so stupid', 'I look terrible').

Strongly disagree	Disagree Somewhat	Neither Agree nor Disagree	Agree Somewhat	Strongly Agree
1	2	3	4	5

10. I often have a hard time understanding why someone would be interested in me romantically or sexually.

Strongly disagree	Disagree Somewhat	Neither Agree nor Disagree	Agree Somewhat	Strongly Agree
1	2	3	4	5

Once you've completed the scale, add together all the numbers assigned to each response you chose, and review the appropriate feedback below.

Your score:

10–25: Your score indicates that you have a fairly poor sense of your self-worth. And the chances are that your ideas about yourself are not really accurate – you may be focusing too much on the negative and ignoring the many positive aspects of who you are as a person. Poor self-worth is something you should consider working on because it can interfere with your interest in and ability to go after challenging goals. It can also make it more difficult for you to find a healthy romantic relationship, with a partner who values you as a person and who treats you well.

26-40: Your score indicates that your sense of self-worth is moderate – lower in some areas and higher in others. Although no one feels they're the best at everything (and, of course, no one actually *is* the best at everything), it's possible that some of your more negative feelings about yourself could be improved by a change of focus, or working harder to accomplish certain goals.

41–50: Your score indicates that you have a fairly positive sense of your self-worth. That's great, because feeling this way can improve your ability to successfully accomplish challenging goals, and to find and maintain a healthy romantic relationship.

SELF-LOVE

Did you know that you are the single most important person in your world?

Imagine that you have completed two important projects at work. The first project is received with praise and accolades. Your boss tells everyone how fabulous you are and that everyone could take a leaf out of your book. The second project is received with criticism and negative comments. Your boss insults you and dismisses your work as a waste of time.

Which of those two situations would get more of your energy and attention? The latter? The negative reaction will be far more impactful than the positive one. It's the result of what psychologists call the **negativity bias**. This is the theory that if there are two similar events, one positive and one negative, the negative one will attract more of your mind's attention.

From the moment you wake until the moment you go to sleep, you are bombarded with more information than your mind can actively process at once. In order for your brain to function in an environment that is packed with information, your mind filters out almost all of the information around you. This is called **attentional filtering**. The interesting thing about this is that a side-effect of the brain's attentional filtering is that the world ends up looking like whatever it is you're focused on. Still confused? Think about how, as you read this, you are not actively paying attention to how your feet feel in your shoes. But now that I have mentioned it, your attention is now on your feet – you're noticing them. That's the attentional filter in action.

Fabulous and incredible as our minds are, they are not very good at processing reality. Your mind is much more likely to focus on what is wrong rather than what's right (the negativity bias). Your mind is forced to filter out almost all of the information it receives in any given situation (attentional filters).

How does this relate to self-care, you ask? Because your mind has a tendency to view *you* as being far less intelligent, capable, good-looking, kind, and worthy of love than you actually are!

Social media only exacerbates this, and as we live in an advertising culture whose main aim is to make you feel bad about yourself unless you're up to date with *all* the latest trends, it's hard to escape viewing ourselves negatively.

Simply put, if you are having trouble loving yourself, there is nothing wrong with you, you just have to change the way you view yourself. Fortunately, loving yourself is a skill, like all the tools I've talked about already, that can be learned and mastered. The first step is accepting that you are important!

Everything in your life stems from your relationship with yourself. Learn to treat yourself like someone worthy of love, respect and compassion, and your life will reflect how you treat yourself. It won't make the stressors vanish in a puff of smoke, but it will allow you to manage yourself in a kinder way. Treat yourself with disrespect, neglect and apathy, and each day will be a struggle just to keep your head above water.

The unfortunate part of all this is that most people never put much energy into their relationship with themselves. They think self-care is on the outside and neglect to love themselves on the inside. They are their own worst critic, and it nearly becomes a full-time job working to ensure they don't love themselves. This may sound slightly dramatic, but just think. If you spoke to your friends the way you speak to yourself in your head, would you have any friends left? It may come as a surprise, but it is very hard to love someone else if you don't love yourself.

By no means am I an expert on fully loving myself – I was once told that 'self-love is a process, not a destination' – but I have come a long way in learning to love myself. Over the years I distracted myself with drugs, alcohol, stress, busyness, bad relationships (lots of them), external validation and pretend happiness in order to not have to face up to the fact I have very little, or no, self-love. What an utter waste of time. I really do wish I had met the me now back in my teens when my self-love started to really diminish.

Really, truly loving yourself is hard, it takes time and effort, but the payoff is worth it and with increased self-love the risk of burnout is reduced.

Think of your relationship with yourself as having four elements:

1. **Day-to-day.** Do you treat yourself like an important person who deserves love and respect, or are you constantly putting unrealistic expectations on yourself? What do your behaviours say about your relationship with yourself?

2. **Your dark side.** Do you accept your dark side (we all have a dark side) when it surfaces? Do you accept the part of you that is negative, lazy, sometimes low, angry and rude? Or do you pretend that everything is grand and life is fabulous? Do you pretend that every day is a good day? None of us likes to think we have dark thoughts, but to not acknowledge and accept them as part of who we are is as damaging as living in blissful ignorance of who you are. Life is full of ups and downs, as are our thoughts and emotions. Embrace them all.

3. **Accepting.** When you honestly see yourself for who you are, both the good and the dark, your imperfections and what makes you perfect and unique, you can start to learn to love yourself without judgement of who you are. It is never too late to become who you truly are. You

can begin accepting who you are, dark side included, and begin to really love yourself.

4. **Your uniqueness.** Every single person was born unique. Your uniqueness can be anything from entertainer, to empathic, to humour, to business intelligence, and everything in between. Learning to love yourself allows you to accept your uniqueness and use it; it's like your own special super power!

THE COMPLICATED RELATIONSHIP BETWEEN FEELINGS AND ACTIONS

One of the things about us humans and our behaviour is that how we feel and how we behave mirrors itself. In other words, if you treat yourself badly, you'll feel bad; If you treat yourself like an amazing person, you'll feel like an amazing person.

Take a minute and think about today. Did your behaviours today mirror the actions of someone who loves themselves?

For most people, if they are being honest, the answer is no. Most people get too little sleep or exercise, eat poorly, work in jobs they hate, and go to great lengths to avoid spending any real time in their own company.

Imagine if you spent today living life loving yourself, how would that look? Take the risk of treating yourself with love and compassion for a month and see what happens.

There is no one set of behaviours that works for everyone. However, the steps below are unusually effective and ones that I talk about regularly throughout this book. They are not complicated, but don't think that because they are simple they won't work – they do! These steps consistently get results, laid out in an order that is congruent with how the heart and mind tend to work. They are exercises to make you question yourself and how your mind works. Use your journal to document how you feel. If you find something that works for you, keep going with it. If not, move on and try another.

1. **Prioritise sleep.** I will say this over and over again – five or six hours' sleep is simply not enough. Between seven and ten hours is the guideline, any less and you'll know about it and anymore and it's counterproductive.

2. **Exercise.** Spend at least 30 minutes a day 7 days a week getting exercise. This can be walking, jogging, lifting, yoga, team sports, playing with the kids, whatever. But do it.

3. **Meditation or silent reflection.** Personally, I practise talking to my Purple Alien (see Week 11).

4. **Express gratitude.** Write down your gratitude for the people you meet and have in your life. It can be someone you know or a stranger you encountered. Write down a few things that you're grateful for each day.

5. **Hold space for your religion or spirituality.** Just because your best friend doesn't go to mass or believe in religion or spirituality, don't let that be the reason you ignore your own beliefs, whatever they are. God, the Universe, Nature, it doesn't matter where you find your spirituality, just honour it.

6. **Eat healthily for you.** Don't keep thinking that food restricting and dieting is the answer to self-love. Eat to make you feel good, eat to nourish your body and eat to celebrate loving yourself!

7. **Set boundaries.** Are you allowing toxic people, activities or habits into your life? If so, slowly start removing them. Use your Wheel of Life to identify what is not working for you and set about changing it.

8. **Play.** Remember how playing made you feel when you were young? Find a way to unleash your inner child, and play!

9.   **Give yourself pep talks throughout the day.** Take a few minutes
      throughout the day to tell yourself you're great. That every small step
      towards loving yourself is to be celebrated.

The more you act like someone who loves themselves, the more you'll feel
like someone who loves themselves.

Week 10

Boundaries

You are getting towards the end of the programme and this week's focus is on setting boundaries and learning one of the most key words you will ever need – no! You will learn the importance of setting personal and professional boundaries, and there are tips on how to begin putting them in place. Along with understanding why saying no is a self-care practice and not a sign of disinterest or rudeness, I will give you lots of tips on how to start getting into the habit of putting you first.

Adhering to your personal boundaries can be difficult unless you are very clear about what they are and are committed to them in order to protect your self-care. There will always be situations and events that will pop up unexpectedly, in your personal and work life, that will challenge you and cause you to forget your boundaries, in turn risking taking on too much and creating unnecessary stress.

That is why knowing what your boundaries are, why they are important to you and how you are going to implement them is essential. Knowing what your personal boundaries are is all very well, but having the confidence to implement them (especially if these are going to be new boundaries you are setting) can be difficult.

I used to keep changing my boundaries to fit different relationships, mainly personal relationships but also work-related ones. Now that I understand that boundaries are about my relationship with myself and my own values, I have stopped changing them at the drop of a hat to suit other people's needs.

Having the courage to live your life by your boundaries can mean the difference between a stressful day or work environment and an empowering one. Boundaries can be applicable to many areas of your life, but the ones I want to highlight are your personal and professional boundaries.

PERSONAL BOUNDARIES

These are the boundaries we set around our personal relationships. These boundaries set the tone for what we allow to happen (and participate in) with our own and others' behaviour. Personal boundaries define how we allow ourselves to be treated (by others, and by ourselves).

Setting personal boundaries is intrinsically linked to our self-esteem. If we feel disempowered or taken advantage of by the relationships around us, our self-esteem is impacted. And as I've said earlier, low self-esteem can impact our health, our stress levels, our personal relationships, as well as how achievable we feel our goals are.

When I learned to know (and implement) my personal boundaries, I started to be able to use those boundaries to create a more empowering life for myself. I learned it was okay to recognise the importance of my health and wellbeing, and that being able to live by my boundaries helped reduce my stress levels.

What are your boundaries? Do you know what they are? Do you have a healthy relationship with saying no? Healthy personal boundaries allow you to become your best self within your personal and professional relationships, as a parent, as an employee, as an employer and as a person.

PROFESSIONAL BOUNDARIES

Setting professional boundaries can feel more daunting due to the hierarchy of authority and structure of most workplaces. However, there are always aspects of professional boundaries that you can control. For example, how you structure your time (see Week 6). There is a phrase I hear more and more often in relation to how people work – the 'instant work environment'. A good example, which I think most people can relate to, would be if you were in the middle of finishing off a task for someone else (your manager) and you received an email with a new request, which was followed by a text message with another request, and at the same time your phone rang. That is an 'instant' work environment. This type of working environment (and it can relate to home life too) makes us feel that we need to respond immediately to all the requests that cross our path. If you are not adhering to your boundaries, you can become overwhelmed by the constant demands and it can also create an environment that allows the 'instant' demands to continue.

This is where boundaries come in. Setting your professional boundaries, *and* communicating them, allows you to take control of your time at work. Be clear in what you are able to do. For example, if you're in the middle of finishing an important task and you are asked to do something else, explain that you are willing to do it but that either (a) you have to finish the task at hand first or (b) if you start working on the second task, it will mean the first will not be finished in time. Be clear in communicating your boundaries. It gives you control.

Learning to set healthy personal and professional boundaries puts you on a road to better health and wellbeing and can help decrease the chances of burnout. Just think about this – 80% of chronic illnesses are caused by lifestyle-related issues. Setting personal and professional boundaries is a simple way to empower yourself, take control of your life and protect your self-care.

STEPS TO SETTING BETTER BOUNDARIES

1. **No boundaries = little self-esteem.** I have already explained how having low self-esteem can increase your chances of burnout. Having a strong set of personal and professional boundaries gives you the power to strengthen your self-esteem. Your boundaries are based on your values. Boundaries define how much or how little you respect yourself. Boundaries are your friend.

2. **Use your core values.** Use the exercise in Week 8 to identify your personal values and use them to figure out what you're comfortable with and what you aren't. For example, I don't like to talk on the phone after 9 p.m., so when I'm at home I set my phone to 'do not disturb' from 9 p.m. until 9 a.m. This allows me to spend time after work with my family, which is one of my personal values. Once you are clear on what matters most to you by understanding your personal values, you can then start setting your boundaries. Just make sure that you communicate this to other people! This is key. Don't focus on setting your boundaries around other people in your life; your boundaries are about you. My phone boundaries are about honouring the fact that I want to spend time with my children, and as an introvert I value my quiet time. This boundary is not about avoiding talking to people, it's about being true to my boundaries in order to value my self-care.

3. **You can't change others, but you can change you.** We cannot change other people. Much as we would like to think we can, we simply cannot and we are also not responsible for what they say, the choices they make or their reactions to life events or things we've said (as long as anything we say is said with love and kindness). Since you can't (and never will) change other people, learn how to change how you deal with them to reduce your stress.

4. **When someone else pushes your boundaries.** Knowing what your boundaries are allows you to plan how to manage yourself when others try and push yours (and they will, because that's life). Decide how you will manage yourself prior to the event. The best way to figure out how to manage yourself when people cross or push your boundaries is to spend some time asking yourself how you will respond, what exactly you will say. Don't leave this part to chance as it will result in you reacting rather than responding and maybe even compromising your boundaries. (Remember: boundaries are about honouring your needs, not about judging other people's choices.)

5. **Let your behaviour, not just your words, speak for you.** As I've said, it is hugely important to communicate your boundaries clearly to people and then let your behaviour around those boundaries do the talking. So if anyone calls me after 9 p.m. and I answer the phone, I am clearly saying 'It's okay to call me after nine' when it is not! By not sticking to my boundary through my behaviour, I am saying one thing and doing another. People will respond to your behaviour, not just your words. The biggest part of boundaries is how clearly you communicate them. You can have set the best boundaries on the planet, but if you do not communicate them clearly, you are going to create some really confusing relationships, both for you and everyone else involved.

Boundaries are based on your personal values and beliefs, so create ones that are realistic and meaningful to you. Be empowered to take control of how you live your life, at home and at work. It doesn't happen overnight, but slowly, over time, you will start to honour your boundaries and others will come to accept them too.

SAYING NO

'Learn to say no to the things that don't matter so we can say yes to the things that we care about.' **Anonymous**

If you are someone who feels the need to please others and put their needs before your own, it can be a very daunting thought, never mind task, to assert yourself to say no. There are many reasons why we are not comfortable with this simple but impactful word. Most of my extended family live or have grown up in the States and one of the behaviours they seem to be extremely comfortable with is the ability to say no! The thought that it might offend the asker doesn't even enter their head. They are comfortable with being able to put their own needs first in order to mind their self-care.

Top tips on how to say no without feeling bad:

- **Be polite.** Just because you are saying you are not going to do something does not mean you have to be rude about it! A simple, 'I'm sorry, I'm not able do this right now' is perfect. You don't need to be overly apologetic or defensive about it, either. Once you start learning to say no, you will reduce the stress and the likelihood of burnout. Remember what I said about the way you think about yourself reflecting how you feel about yourself? Well, the same is true here – you teach people how you want to be treated. Standing firm and saying no is a way to show others you're not at everyone's beck and call, both at work and at home!

- **Have the manners to listen.** People often don't ask for something unless it is really important to them. While that doesn't give them the green light to expect you to say yes, it does mean they are requesting your help because they might really need it. And in my experience, for some people, asking for help is as difficult as saying no. So have the manners to take the time to listen to what they are asking. If you don't have the time there and then, arrange a time when you can give them your full attention. Don't half listen and say no when you don't even know what they're asking. Listen to their request even if you already have it in your head that you are going to say no.

- **You can think about it.** If you are uncomfortable with the idea of saying no immediately, take your time and think about it. If you want time to think about the request, or just simply have some time to see if this is something you want to do but you don't have the time right now, simply saying, 'I need to check my diary (with my partner, boss, dog, cat ...); I'll get back to you.' Remember, though, you need to ensure you don't start spending too much time overthinking it; get back to the person as soon as possible with your decision. If you must decline in an email or text, that's okay. This tip helps you avoid getting pressured into over-stretching yourself and taking on too much.

- **Establish your priorities.** Knowing what your priorities or goals are provides you with the strength and focus to decide whether saying yes will distract you or inhibit you. I work from home and when I am seeing clients, my door is closed and my family know I'm working, however, there seems to be an unspoken assumption that when I'm on my laptop working, I'm free game for 'chats'. My darling mother has the key to my house and regularly (daily!) lets herself in to 'drop something off'. This, she feels, entitles her to a cuppa and a chat. If I worked in an office environment I'm not so sure how often she would visit me like this! Previously I would allow myself to be distracted or let her presence inhibit me from getting through my work. Now I have clear priorities for my day and am politely able to say no to her requests. Don't get me wrong, I'm always happy to see her and have a cuppa, but when saying yes to her puts stress on my workload, being able to say no without guilt means that I get my work done and she doesn't feel rejected.

➡ **Be fast and firm with your response.** Although I suggested earlier that you should allow yourself time to think, if you feel strongly about saying no, don't hesitate about working up the courage to say no. If you know immediately that saying yes to a request is going to negatively impact on your time or will result in being over-stressed and overstretched, tell them. Don't moan about it, just make your answer is clear and fact-based. This gives the person a chance to ask for help from someone else.

Saying no is powerful and for those who are people pleasers it can be a game changer. Reclaiming your voice and using it with kindness and self-respect – what could be better?

Week 11

Daily tools for big change: mindfulness, gratitude and journalling

Week 11 is probably one of my favourite weeks, and one I work through with all my clients, whatever issues they might present with. Mindfulness, gratitude and journalling, what I refer to as 'daily tools for big change', are tools that anyone can implement in their lives. All three practices are backed up by research and have been proven to reduce stress and help foster greater self-care. I explain how you can bring mindfulness into your daily life without it having to take up extra time and how daily gratitude lets you reframe how you view your world.

MINDFULNESS

'In mindfulness one is not only restful and happy, but alert and awake.' **Thich Nhat Hanh**

There are some tools that, if used regularly, can have a huge impact on your day. They don't need to take up a lot of time and after a few weeks they will become a habit.

Mindfulness is one of those lovely ideas that I used to think I had to have lots of time in my day to actually do. Not so! So many of my clients secretly raise their eyes to heaven when I mention mindfulness and meditation. The idea that practising mindfulness is only going to add to their already stressed lives is sometimes more than they can handle. I show clients how they can incorporate mindfulness into what they already do rather than asking them to find new pockets of time they don't currently have. Amazingly, though, most of my clients who do start to practise mindfulness have gone on to carve out time in their day to dedicate to mindfulness.

Twenty minutes of meditation is equal to a two-hour nap.

Before I tell you what mindfulness is, let me first tell you what it is *not*.

- It is not purely for yogis and hippies.
- It is not religious, although it has its roots in Buddhism. It is not a religious cult.
- It does not require hours of practice.
- Nor does it require you to sit cross-legged and chant.
- It most certainly is not a waste of time.

Mindfulness is the basic human ability to be fully present, aware of where we are and what we're doing, and not overly reactive or overwhelmed by what's going on around us.

It is also important to note:

- **Anyone can do it.** Mindfulness practice is something everyone can do – men, women, children, grandparents. Everyone can benefit and it's easy to learn.

- **It's a way of living.** Mindfulness is more than just a daily five-minute practice. It brings awareness and caring into everything we do, and it cuts down needless stress. Even a little mindfulness a day goes a long way to making our lives better.

- **It's evidence-based.** We don't have to take the benefits of mindfulness on faith. Both science and research demonstrate its positive benefits for our health, happiness, work and relationships.

You probably already practise mindfulness in some way and just don't realise it.

CONOR'S STORY

Recently I worked with a lovely man who was a volunteer on a TV documentary called *Stressed*, which aired on RTÉ1 in May 2018. Conor is a chef and owns a restaurant and two cafés. He's in his early 30s, extremely busy, has a partner and two young children, sometimes works seven days a week and is not a great delegator at work. One of the biggest stressors that came up for Conor was paperwork. He utterly hates it, but as he is not great at delegating at work he ends up doing most of it himself. Splitting his time between his two cafés and restaurant, family life and the added stress of trying to keep on top of all the paperwork for three different venues – which, unbeknownst to him, was his biggest stressor – meant that he had very little time for his self-care. Whenever I met Conor I could see he was always thinking ahead, he was very rarely in the present moment. Another behaviour I noticed with Conor was his reluctance to write things down. This meant that he was constantly trying to keep in his mind lots of thoughts, ideas and lists of things he had to do all at the same time. One of the issues with this way of thinking is that it creates very little space for new thoughts to form or to allow time for his mind to quieten down. We have a very small space in our brain for short-term memory storage; most of our memory space is for long-term retention.

Because Conor was, initially, resisting writing things down, he found he would get quite stressed over small things that happened in his day that he didn't have the brain space to think about or figure out how to resolve. Working with Conor to create a realistic self-care plan that would be easy to adhere to and not something he would see as an extra chore in his already busy life was really important for him.

To begin with I spent time with him talking through his day. Even though there could be many differences every day, there was still a beginning, middle and end to each day. Seeing how Conor managed his day was important in being able to help him restructure and change some of his behaviours. I looked at how he could incorporate mindfulness into his day. Most days Conor would drive to a park in Dublin for a 20-minute break from work, where he would sit in the car and read the paper. He found that he was more tired after doing this than feeling recharged and ready for an evening of work. I suggested he try mindful walking, a practice that he could incorporate into his day during his break time. Mindful walking is about focusing on your breathing while taking in the sounds, smells and sights around you. Like all mindfulness, it is about being in the present moment, not thinking about the past or the future. After a few attempts, I could see that it wasn't quite working for Conor, and although he very kindly walked with me, he was not really comfortable with the process, felt that he was doing it wrong and put expectations on himself that added to his stress!

I was determined to get Conor to see the benefits of mindfulness. It wasn't until I saw him working in the kitchen of his restaurant that I saw that even though he didn't realise it, he was already well practised in the art of mindfulness. In what seemed like a big stressor for Conor, a stressful situation ended up being a positive twist of faith. A chef in his restaurant went on holidays and Conor was left with no one to run the kitchen. While this could have been another stress to add to his life, the reality was very different. Conor hadn't spent proper time in the kitchen in quite a while and had forgotten that the reason he opened his own restaurant was because of his love of cooking. Conor in the kitchen was a mindful man! When he was cooking he was totally present in where he was and what he was doing. He was not aware of the tables or the customers; all that mattered was the task at hand. And that is mindfulness – being present in the here and now.

When he was able to understand the concept and realise that he already practised it, it made it easier for him to be able to incorporate it into other parts of his life. This is my point. Mindfulness does not have to be separate from your day-to-day living. Make it part of your everyday life. While there may be nothing you can do to eliminate life's stressors, by engaging in mindfulness you can avoid letting these challenges affect you.

MY PURPLE ALIEN

Anyone who has heard me speak at events will have heard me talk about my Purple Alien. Sitting outside my client room is a beautiful golden Buddha a very close friend gave me one Christmas. She had heard me talking about how much I wanted to create a special space in my house where I could meditate. This greatly amused her, but she still bought it for me! The reason it amused her is simple: she had no idea when I, as a single mum of two busy boys, with a full client load, speaking events, various other projects and a love of having an open house, was seriously going to sit down and meditate. She was right! At the moment I have to work at incorporating mindfulness into my life rather than finding time I don't have right now; hence the golden Buddha sitting outside my office and greeting my clients. I did, however, find a different way to practise my mindfulness. I created a Purple Alien. My Purple Alien is a visual friend (sort of like a childhood imaginary friend) who lives in outer space and acts as a source of grounding for me. At least once a day when I am walking, I switch my phone to silent and visualise connecting to my Alien's mind. He is fascinated by my world but unfortunately as he lives in outer space he can't see my life on earth. My job, on my various walks, is to describe everything I see to him. This can be the colour of house doors, cars parked in driveways, leaves on the trees, flowers blooming, dogs in windows. Anything and everything I see I mentally relay to him as I see it. Because here's the thing. If I'm consciously aware of my surroundings, the smells, sounds and sights, I'm not thinking about what to cook for dinner, or what bills I have to pay; I am being in the present moment. It's an excellent method for becoming more aware of your surroundings, bringing yourself back to alertness, taking a step away from your anxieties and experiencing what is happening around you. I've had clients and people who have heard me speak email me after hearing me talk about my Purple Alien to tell me how easy it is to use this method to start practising mindfulness. They don't all use my Purple Alien, some use relatives or friends as their anchor, but whatever or whoever you use, try it out the next time you go for a walk!

Mindfulness, no matter how you achieve it, can kick start the process of regaining control of your life.

For those who prefer guided mindfulness practices, there are two great apps for both iPhone and android – Calm and Headspace.

GRATITUDE

Yes, being grateful does change how you feel!

Modern life can be stressful, we have established that, but what if you could click your fingers and go from feeling that life is an uphill struggle to waking up each morning with a sense of knowing you're going to be okay? This is possible through the practice of gratitude, the simple art of saying thank you, of focusing on what you do have and not on what you don't.

Research has shown that those who practise gratitude see immediate improvements in their lives, from feeling happier and sleeping better to experiencing improved physical health and the achievement of life goals, all by simply saying 'I am grateful for ...'.

Gratitude is not about focusing on materialistic elements of our lives; it is about acknowledging the small things around us and being grateful for them.

So what is the best way to practice gratitude? Quite simply, it's whatever works for you. I often give my clients journals to write in and suggest they write down things they are grateful for each day. Start small by writing a list of three things you are grateful for; it can be warm weather, someone who smiled at you or the dinner you get to eat later tonight that's been lovingly made by someone else! As you continue practising gratitude, you will more than likely be amazed by the multitude of things you find to appreciate in your life. Gratitude journalling has been proved to be effective at overcoming several psychological challenges.

The benefits of practising gratitude are endless:

- Gratitude makes you happier.
- Gratitude makes other people like you.
- Gratitude makes you healthier.
- Gratitude boosts your career.
- Gratitude strengthens your emotions.
- Gratitude develops your personality.
- Gratitude makes you more optimistic.
- Gratitude reduces materialism.
- Gratitude increases spirituality.
- Gratitude makes you less self-centred.
- Gratitude increases your self-esteem.
- Gratitude improves your sleep.
- Gratitude helps you live longer.
- Gratitude increases your energy levels.
- Gratitude makes you more likely to exercise.
- Gratitude helps you bounce back from challenges.
- Gratitude makes you feel good.

- Gratitude reduces feelings of envy.

- Gratitude helps you relax.

- Gratitude makes you friendlier.

- Gratitude helps your relationships.

- Gratitude makes you look good.

- Gratitude helps you network.

- Gratitude increases your goal achievement.

- Gratitude improves your decision-making.

- Gratitude increases your productivity.

JOURNALLING

'You want to make something a fast reality – write it down.' **Abraham Hicks**

At the beginning of this book I suggested that you start journalling. There are so many incredible ways writing helps with both identifying burnout and recovering from it. Most people shy away from writing as they feel they aren't good enough, or their grammar isn't great, or what on earth would they write or, worse still, 'What if someone found it?' Journalling allows the brain to generate clarity and congruence. Writing down what is going on in our head allows us to identify what is real and what is not. And in turn it will give you the ability to see what needs to be changed in your life and figure out what is working and not working for you.

Journalling also helps clear emotions and reduces stress – imagine that! In relation to stress, journalling helps by:

- reducing mental chaos

- increasing focus

- creating a greater level of order, action and letting go

- encouraging reflection

- taking personal responsibility

- challenging our thoughts vs. realities.

The list of benefits is endless. We can hold on to incredibly negative thoughts in our minds that can stay put for days or even years. When we learn to write honestly and with personal responsibility, it frees up so much head space for us to move on, let go and create the environment we want.

I would recommend journalling with pen and paper rather than using a phone, laptop or iPad. As we get older we struggle at retaining information. We can forget a lot of what we hear and read unless it strikes an emotional chord with us. Journalling (writing the things in our head down) increases brain development and memory, something that typing into our phones or our laptops does not do. According to neuroscience, a different part of the brain is activated when we hear things than when we write them down. When we hear information our brain (memory) does not file it away under important or not important, it just files it away under general information. However, when we write things down it allows our brain (memories) to store the information in different files such as important and not important. This allows us to target the important stuff and either let go of or file away the unimportant stuff that has been clogging up our minds.

Okay, now what? As with all of these things, there is no right or wrong way to journal. The only thing you need is pen, paper and to trust yourself.

- **Use pen and paper.** I've already explained why, but it's also more difficult to flick through social media with a notebook! If you like nice stationery, splash out and buy something fancy, but a bargain notebook and pen will do just as good a job.

- **Create a habit.** If you say to yourself you'll write every day but don't schedule in the time to do it, it will become another thing that adds stress to your day, something that doesn't get done. And that is not beneficial to anyone. Creating habits needs triggers. For me, writing is an evening habit as I've finished working with my private clients, kids are sorted, kitchen clean and technology put away in the drawer for tomorrow. Bedtime tea and ten minutes of writing at the kitchen table and off to bed. I don't write in bed as my bed is for reading and sleeping and if I fall asleep reading that's fine, but falling asleep writing isn't! I've always had my last cup of tea in peace in the kitchen, so all I did was attach a new habit to an existing one. Win–win.

● **Slow down.** Sometimes we can be scared of our own thoughts and so we fill our lives so full of 'stuff' that we don't have to hear our minds. With that in mind then, the thought of actually sitting down and writing can be mind-blowingly scary, a total waste of time or just utterly self-indulgent and therefore it falls back under the category of 'stressors'. But take those thoughts away and realise that it is scientifically proven that journalling can reduce time-wasting and stress by clearing your mind and giving your thoughts clarity. If journalling was a pill prescribed by the doctor and it was free, everyone would be queuing up to get a prescription!

● **Don't judge yourself.** Don't get caught up in judging yourself and how your journal should read. This is not an English essay you are going to be marked on; it's a tool to create a better way of living.

● **Make it work for you.** Some days I write away. I don't notice the time as my mind happily offloads on to the pages. Some days I write in bullet point form and crawl up to bed. Neither is right or wrong. I don't beat myself up that I haven't written a ten-page masterpiece of carefully curated thoughts. I make my journalling work for me. Do the same – make it work for you. And enjoy it.

○ **Journalling increases your gratitude.** Gratitude journalling is scientifically proven to overcome trauma. The benefits are endless.

In his 2012 Person of the Year interview with *Time* magazine, President Obama described the incredible power of writing: 'In my life, writing has been an important exercise to clarify what I believe, what I see, what I care about, what my deepest values are. The process of converting a jumble of thoughts into coherent sentences makes you ask tougher questions.'

Week 12

Creating your new Life Map

T his is the last week of the burnout recovery programme and I
hope that by now, with the help of the weekly steps in this book,
you are starting to feel better and have a greater understanding of
who you are and how you can create the changes you need in order to
ensure you don't find yourself heading towards burnout again. This week
is about taking stock of all the resources you've learned so far in each of
the different weeks and creating your new Life Map. I explain why getting
visual (and realistic) about your future allows you to be focused on living
your life in the here and now. And finally, there is a section for you to write
your own self-care plan. Throughout this book, using personal stories and
some clients' stories, I've shown you what self-care plans can look like, but
everyone has different likes and dislikes, and what works for one person
might not work for another. Take your time and use the 'layers' you've
learned each week and have already put into practice to write down what
your self-care plan is, and start putting yourself first.

Last year I started to get visual about the future that I wanted. I had a rough
idea of what I wanted my future to look like, but to be honest I was a little
scared about putting it down on paper. What would happen if it didn't turn
out the way I wanted it to? In getting more visual about what I wanted,

I started to get a clearer understanding of what specifically I wanted my future to look and feel like. I allowed myself to really think about what I wanted and had a bit of fun doing it. It felt less overwhelming and more fun to visually map out my life rather than have it all stored up in my brain. It also made me confront a few lingering fears that were stopping me moving forward. I let go of the Life Map I thought was mine and worked at creating one that's best suited to me.

Before doing this, I want to point out a few obvious things.

- **You can't control your future.** Mapping out your future does not mean that things will happen exactly the way you want them to. The beauty of life is in the unexpected and unplanned events. But I don't think it's bad to have a vision of what you would like for your future. I think there is value in wanting things even if it doesn't turn out exactly that way. And we can change our minds about our future plans over and over again. That's okay too!

- **Belongings aren't what is important.** Being happy, or happier, is the most important part of your life now and in the future. However, working towards having physical belongings, such as owning your own home, is fine too. Just don't put all your focus or effort into having them. At the end of the day, belongings are just belongings and it's the relationships that you build with yourself and others that mean the most.

- **The doing is more important than the dreaming.** As I said, I don't believe that simply mapping out your future is going to make it so. I believe you have to work hard at what you want and be clear as to why you want it, trust in your vision for yourself and own it. By no means do I believe that you can sit around visualising and expect your new Life Map to miraculously happen. You have to put positive energy into making it happen. Mapping it out can help point you in the right direction, it can encourage you and show you what's important for you, but it can't and won't do the work for you.

- **Unrealistic goals are not helpful.** Visualising winning the Lotto is not a realistic goal for your Life Map. Be realistic, and be honest with yourself.

- **Big priorities come first.** Last year I set three big goals for my new Life Map. There are smaller goals dotted along the way, but my main priority has been focusing on my top three big ones. There are so many things I want in my Life Map; it's important to remember it's the big things that get you closer to your goals. Start with your biggest priorities and go from there.

Here are the reasons I believe it's helpful to get visual and plan out your future:

- You're focusing on checking in, asking yourself what it is you want and what is important to you.

- This helps you realise what it is you don't want and what is not important to you.

- You're more likely to figure out how to get there, because you know where you want to go.

- You're allowing yourself to visualise yourself achieving your goals.

- You're more in tune to feeling when you're not on the right path (and, like Google Maps, you can redirect yourself).

- You're able to turn opportunities down when they don't serve you (saying no to things in order to say yes to what matters to you).

- You're able to seek guidance from those who have already done what you aim to do.

> Focus on how you want to feel before you think about what you want to physically have. Remind yourself **why** you want what you want in life. Why does it matter to you? Why do you care about it?

Your whys are important, so hold on to them. Businesses use mission statements to guide everything they do as a company. If it doesn't fit the mission, it has no place in their business plan. The same should go for you and your life.

When you're evaluating what is most important, go into every aspect of your life and think about how you'd like to feel and what you envision.

Here are some of the areas of life you should think about:

- home
- friendships
- romantic relationships
- family
- career

... and so on.

The more you explore this, with a realistic and open mind, the closer you can be to working on getting where you want to be. There are a variety of ways in which you can do this.

DESIGN YOUR VISION BOARD

No matter who we are or what we do, we all have needs, wants and desires. However, with busy lifestyles, work commitments and life pressures, keeping sight of our dreams and goals can be easier said than done. Our dreams are unique to our own personalities and beliefs; therefore, it's important that we give ourselves time to focus on what we truly want out of life. A vision board is a collection of pictures, words and affirmations that offer positive reinforcement for whatever it is that you want to achieve. Using a vision board can let you see an overall view of what you want in your life. It's like a picture story book of your Life Map, your One Thing, your self-care and your future vision all rolled into one. It can be words and affirmations that resonate and mean something to you, pictures of places you'd like to visit or have visited and that mean something to you. There is no right or wrong way to create your vision board and there are loads of online resources to help you get started at being creative. Grab some magazines, find words or sayings you love and create your vision board. If placing it somewhere you can see every day is something you're not comfortable with, take a photo of it and use it as the screen saver on your phone or computer!

WRITE A LETTER TO YOUR FUTURE SELF

This was a big step towards becoming more visual in 2015. I wrote a letter to myself as if I was writing to myself three years later. I talked about my accomplishments and what I was doing. I went down the list of life categories (listed above) and talked about how proud I was of the life I built for myself. Writing about what you desire your life to be in a few years gives you the mindset to start working to make them happen.

Whenever I ask clients to write letters to their younger selves, they physically baulk at the idea! And much as this is a great exercise to do, for the purpose of this book I'd like you to write a letter to your future self. A letter that you write now, having read and worked through this book, and read at some point in the future, a handwritten snapshot of your life as you view it now, your true self and your emotions *right here and now*.

You may ask, 'What is the point of writing (and reading) a letter to my future self? How on earth do I go about writing it and what will I even say?' Writing a letter to your future self which you could open in a year, two years or even five years, is a great way to remind yourself of where you are right now and what goals you're setting for yourself personally and professionally. It allows you to see if you have made progress with your goals.

Writing these letters is also a perfect exercise for building your self-awareness, and it lets you look back and see how you have changed and evolved as a person – not just in what you have done and achieved, but in how you interact and react to the world around you through the changes you have taken responsibility for making. It is a wonderful exercise in which to incorporate gratitude, too; it helps you be aware of all the good things that you have, and that have happened in your life, however big or small, and be grateful for them. Think about what you are grateful for now when you write your letter, and you'll be reminded of them in the future.

The experience of writing a letter to your future self will always be unique for each person. It's personal and can be emotional. Make a deal with yourself when writing that you will focus on what is good in your life, the changes you have made or are in the process of making. It's okay to reference regrets you may have; just make sure you are able to see how you could use those regrets to your advantage.

What to write about?

- Start by giving yourself some advice. Write your letter using the second person to make it more personal and direct.

- What hopes do you hold for yourself in the future? What are your professional goals? Your romantic ones? Intellectual? Financial? Spiritual? Personal? Be as specific as you can – the more specific you are, the more likely you are to achieve your goals.

- What fears and obstacles do you currently have in your life that you want to change?

- What traits of your personality do you know will help you, now and always?

- How strongly do you believe in your own personal strengths?

- What are you excited about? What does your ideal life look like?

- Who are the three most important people in your life (if there are more, write them all down!) and why?

- How would you react if you met your future self? What would you say?

And finally, in what ways are you going to love your future self, no matter what, no matter how different the future is from what you expect?

When you've written your letter, you can either put it away or give it to someone you trust to mind it. At a specified time, open it and reflect on where you are and how much has changed. Doing this every few years allows you to look back on what you've done but also to look to the future using all the tools and practices you have in the now. It's part of your self-love tool kit.

YOUR SELF-CARE PLAN

This section is yours to write. I hope that in reading this book you have gained a better understanding of burnout, that if you are feeling close to or deeply entrenched in it, you can use some of the tools in this book to help kick start your recovery and put in place a plan to ensure that it doesn't happen again.

Admitting you are suffering from burnout is not easy – even the thought of saying it may make you feel more stressed. Remember, burnout is not about not being able to cope with life, it's about learning the tools to be able to manage it.

Today I am going to ... _____

_____

_____

_____

_____

_____

Afterword

Quick tips

To finish, I've summarised my tips for preventing burnout. Much as I'd love to say, 'Just drop everything and go and live on an isolated island in peace and solitude', it's not the answer!

Understanding your behaviours and using the tools and exercises I've shown you to help you make the changes you need for you are your responsibility. No one else can do it for you.

✓ Be aware of your physical, mental and emotional state. Listen to what your body is telling you. Trust it, it doesn't sugar-coat how you feel. If you feel overwhelmed, physically tired or emotional, what can you do about it?

✓ Rather than focusing on how stressed you feel, identify what specifically is causing you stress. Keep asking yourself the question until you get to the root cause. Sometimes we are so overwhelmed we feel that every single thing in life is stressing us out. Generally speaking, there are usually some areas in life that are working well. Use the Wheel of Life as a tool to help you identify the source of your stress.

✓ Good, healthy food sustains your body. It helps your body and mind cope with short bursts of stressful periods. View healthy eating as ensuring that your bank of health is topped up and therefore can cope with unexpected stressors that come your way. Healthy eating is one of the four basics that support your wellbeing.

✓ Be mindful of your alcohol consumption, along with coffee and cigarettes. All of these are simulants and can trigger the releases of cortisol. If you are stressed and burnt-out, extra cortisol is the last thing you need.

✓ Cut back on your coffee intake. Drinking coffee late in the afternoon/early evening affects your sleep.

✓ Smoking has absolutely no benefits. There is nothing to be gained by smoking and an awful lot to be lost by it. I'm not lecturing, I smoked 20 a day for many years. If you smoke, you know the reality.

✓ If drinking in moderation is not damaging you or those around you, great – enjoy yourself! However, if you notice that you are becoming more dependent on alcohol as a perceived de-stressor then it may be time to look at how you view your relationship with it. This is your body. Using stimulants as de-stressors does not work.

✓ Exercise. Simply put, exercise promotes physical, mental and emotional health. It's not about running marathons or being a seven-days-a-week gym member. Thirty minutes of strong walking a day is perfect. Walk with a friend and add in social connection; walk alone without your phone and practice some mindfulness; even listen to a podcast that uplifts you or makes you laugh. Whatever you do, make it part of your daily life. Your body will thank you.

✓ Make eating away from your desk part of your work boundaries. Take a step away from your desk and enjoy your lunch. I doubt your job spec said you must eat your lunch at your desk every day. Don't let other people's actions and choices influence your self-care.

✓ Take mini-breaks at work. This is also applicable to being at home. Our body responds better to short bursts of work. Students are advised to study for a maximum of 50 minutes with a 10-minute break before resuming. The same applies to work. This allows you to move your body and refresh your mind.

✓ Manage your relationship with technology. Be present with those you are with in social settings. Put your phone down. Switch off the TV. Set the out-of-office function. Reclaim your time.

✓ Be kind to yourself, kind but firm. Recognise what you are good at and focus on it. Equally, recognise what you are weak at and ask for help. You cannot be good at everything!

✓ Celebrate your achievements, both personal and professional. Be your biggest fan. Sometimes others don't know how big a deal it may be for you to implement the changes you are making. Don't wait for someone else to congratulate you – do it yourself.

✓ Manage your sleep. Getting a good night's sleep doesn't make the stressors go away, but it gives you the foundations to be able to manage yourself better in the situations you find yourself in. It gives you clarity, energy and lifts your mood.

✓ Watch how you react around others. Does your reaction to stress create stress in those around you?

✓ There is no such thing as perfect. Perfectionism is one of the highest triggers for burnout. Do the best you can and trust your gut.

✓ Learn to say no. Say yes to the things you care about and, whenever you can, say no.

✓ Identify your non-negotiables, such as your family, work, pets, or maybe sports, and your negotiables, any obligations that take away from them. Do a life audit and clear the clutter in your life that is causing you stress.

✓ Make time to have fun. Laugh. Be silly.

✓ Ask for help. If you need help in any area of your life, ask for it. Asking for help is not a sign of weakness, it is a sign of strength.

✓ Above all, treat and speak to yourself as you would to your best friend. Be the kindest person you can be to the most important person in your life. You.

Resources

You can find all of the resources and exercises in this book at www.twistingthejar.com. Some more are listed below.

Burnout tests:

Mind Tools – http://mindtools.com/stress/brn/burnoutSelfTest.htm

Joe Robinson Optimal Performance – http://worktolive.info/burnout-prevention

Minnesota State University – www.mnsu.edu/activities/leadership/toolbox/handout_burnout.pdf

Stress tests:

Mind Tools – www.mindtools.com/pages/article/newTCS_82.htm

Psychology Today – www.psychologytoday.com/intl/tests

Depression:

Your Mental Health – www.yourmentalhealth.ie

Aware – www.aware.ie

Samaritans – www.samaritans.org/news/free-call-samaritans-ireland

Mindfulness apps:

Headspace

Calm

Counselling and psychotherapy:

National Association for Pastoral Counselling and Psychotherapy –
www.napcp.ie

Irish Association for Counselling and Psychotherapy – www.iacp.ie

Cognitive behavioural therapy online courses and information:

Moodgym – https://moodgym.com.au

Living Life – www.llttf.com

Aware – www.aware.ie/education/life-skills-online-programme/

Personality tests:

Myers–Briggs – www.myersbriggs.org

Human Metrics – www.humanmetrics.com

Discover Your Type – http://discover-your-type.com

Nutrition:

Orla Walsh Nutrition – http://orlawalshnutrition.ie/

References

Bain, L. J. et al. (2008). 'Healthy brain aging: A meeting report from the Sylvan M. Cohen Annual Retreat of the University of Pennsylvania Institute on Aging.' *Alzheimers & Dementia*, 4(6), 443–446.

Burton, N. (2015). *Heaven and Hell – The Psychology of the Emotions.* Oxford: Acheron Press.

Deloitte (2016) Global Mobile Consumer Survey: Ireland 2016.

Harvard Health (2010). 'The health benefits of strong relationships.' Available at: www.health.harvard.edu/newsletter_article/the-health-benefits-of-strong-relationships

Huffington, A. S. (2017). *The Sleep Revolution: Transforming your Life, One Night at a Time.* New York: Harmony Books.

Keating, A. (2018). *The Secret Lives of Adults.* Dublin: Gill Books

Keller, G. and Papasan, J. (2013). *The ONE Thing: The Surprisingly Simple Truth behind Extraordinary Results.* Austin: Bard Press

Kondo, M. (2014). *The Life-changing Magic of Tidying Up: The Japanese Art of Decluttering and Organizing.* Berkeley: Ten Speed Press

Lally, P., Jaarsveld, C. H., Potts, H. W., & Wardle, J. (2009). 'How are habits formed: Modelling habit formation in the real world.' *European Journal of Social Psychology*, 40(6), 998–1009.

Maslach, C., Jackson, S.E. & Leiter, M.P. (1996–2016). *Maslach Burnout Inventory Manual (Fourth Edition)*. Menlo Park, CA: Mind Garden, Inc.

Maslow, A. H. (1943). 'A theory of human motivation.' *Psychological Review,* 50(4), 370–396.

Myers, I. B., & Myers, P. B. (1995). *Gifts Differing: Understanding Personality Type*. Mountain View, CA: Consulting Psychologists Press.

Ophir, E., Nass, C. and Wagner, A. D. (2009). 'Cognitive control in media multitaskers.' *PNAS,* 106 (37) 15583–15587

Selye, H. (1984). *The Stress of Life*. New York: McGraw-Hill.

WHO (2017) ICD-10: The 10th Revision of the International Classification of Diseases.

Xie, L., et al. (2013). 'Sleep drives metabolite clearance from the adult brain.' *Science,* 342(6156), 373–377.